Most of the UK's freshwater resources are stored naturally as groundwater. About one-third of the public water supply is taken from this source and in the drier, south-east region, many communities are totally dependant upon it. Although hidden from view, groundwater plays a central role in our environment, maintaining wetlands and river flows through prolonged dry periods. However, to many people who rely upon it, groundwater remains a subject of mystery — even folklore.

This book attempts to demystify the subject. It describes how and where groundwater occurs; how it is used and how it is cared for. The risks to its natural pristine quality from the activities of man are also explained, as well as its dual role of preserving the natural environment while providing a large proportion of the water supply to industrial and domestic users. The need for concerted action to protect and conserve groundwater, both its quality and quantity, is emphasised for this most valuable of natural assets.

- **Groundwater is a vital national asset**

- **Groundwater constitutes the largest volume of freshwater in the UK:**

  A volume many times larger than the storage in surface reservoirs

- **Groundwater maintains river flows and preserves wetlands during droughts**

- **Groundwater is vulnerable to slow insiduous pollution as a result of human activities**

- **Protection of groundwater to maintain its quality is essential**

GR...
our ...

Cover: Photo montage of the many facets of groundwater; the Crocodile Spring at Compton Abdale in the Cotswolds; contamination of the River Esk in East Lothian and artesian flow from a borehole in the Chalk in Dorset.

The booklet is written at two levels of understanding. A general account, printed in black, is provided under each main heading and may be read separately as a continuous text. This is supplemented by more detailed reviews of important issues, together with case studies; these are printed in blue.

Setting the scene

The importance of groundwater is easily overlooked. It is a hidden asset, out-of-sight and out-of-mind, and yet for many communities in the United Kingdom, and indeed many other parts of the world, it is the only source of water supply.

Groundwater occurs in permeable rocks, known as aquifers, which are at least partly saturated as a result of the infiltration of rainfall. Water flows between the small grains that make up an aquifer or in the many fine cracks that intersect it. The water is filtered during its slow passage through the ground, thus ensuring the good quality and consistent chemical composition of groundwater in its natural state. Uncontaminated groundwater

***D**ry valley in the Chalk in the Chiltern Hills. Dry valleys are a feature of the Chalk's landscape. They were excavated by rivers during the Ice Age when the land surface was frozen and hence impermeable. The Chalk is more fractured and therefore more permeable below valleys including dry valleys.*

requires minimal treatment prior to distribution as drinking water.

Groundwater emerges from aquifers at springs or can be pumped from wells or boreholes. By means of springs, aquifers drain naturally into rivers and provide the entire flow in dry periods. The discharge from aquifers also helps to conserve wetlands. The abstraction of groundwater for water supply reduces the natural discharge and this can have a deleterious effect on aquatic environments. When groundwater is developed for water supply the needs of these environments must be considered.

Aquifers and the groundwater they contain are vulnerable to pollution. For generations we discarded our wastes with little concern for the long-term safety of groundwater resources. However, aquifers do not have an infinite capacity for absorbing and neutralising wastes. This began to be realised in the early 1970s

when the discovery of drums of cyanide in a refuse tip in the Midlands focused attention on the potential risk.

The pollution of groundwater is insidious, generally unsuspected, for it occurs slowly, almost imperceptibly; it may take years for it to become apparent in a water supply. Once an aquifer is polluted, remedial treatment is expensive and may not even be feasible. Contamination of aquifers increases the cost of a water supply. We need to be aware of the risk of polluting groundwater supplies and to understand the processes which can lead to their contamination.

Over the years there has been a trend from a dependence for water supply on individual wells, to the regional development of entire aquifers by well-fields. Groundwater is now being over-exploited in some areas. Water levels are falling and in a number of coastal areas sea water is intruding into aquifers. But under some of our cities, because of a change in

the pattern of groundwater use, levels are now rising leading to drainage problems.

The modern management of a large aquifer is a complex task, more so than that of a surface reservoir. Information is required about variations in the permeability and storage capacity of the rocks, the sources of replenishment, and the positions of the various natural outlets, as well as the effect of pumping from wells and boreholes.

The science of hydrogeology provides the basis for understanding aquifers and groundwater, an understanding that requires the interaction of many disciplines — including that of geologists, engineers, physicists, chemists, microbiologists and mathematicians. The purpose of this booklet is to describe how these disciplines have contributed to an awareness of the nature and occurrence of groundwater, how it is developed, why we need to appreciate the risks which challenge the ideal of sustainable use, and why we should be prepared to play a part in preserving the quality of groundwater for our own use and that of future generations.

Our grandfathers knew it was necessary to site the cess-pit downhill from the well. This simple truism is often overlooked in today's society. It is also a basic fact of modern life that 'if you spill it you may drink it'.

Groundwater in the hydrological cycle. Part of the rainfall returns to the atmosphere through evaporation and transpiration by vegetation, and part flows over the ground. The remainder infiltrates aquifers and replenishes groundwater storage. Groundwater flows through aquifers to outlets in rivers, at springs and in the sea. Springs occur where the water table intersects the ground surface, as in valleys and along coastlines, and where water overflows from an aquifer where it overlies a less permeable rock.

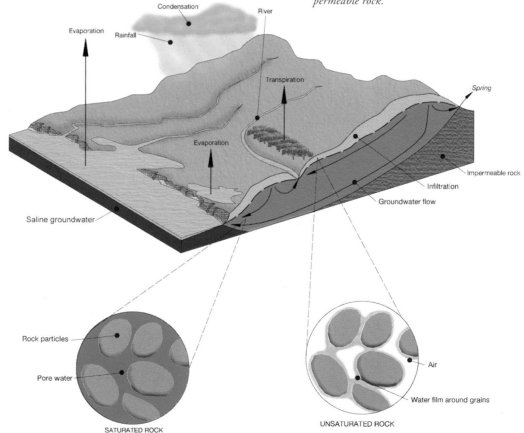

3

What is groundwater?

When a hole is dug in permeable rocks, at a particular depth water begins to flow in. The surface of the water that accumulates in the hole is the water table and the water in the ground below the water table is groundwater.

The variations in the shape of the water table reflect the topography in a subdued form. The water table is near the ground in valleys, actually intersecting the ground surface where rivers, lakes and marshes occur, but it is at much greater depths below hills.

The pore spaces of rocks are saturated with water below the water table and groundwater is said to occur in the saturated zone. Immediately above the water table, water is drawn up into pore spaces by capillary forces into a thin zone called the capillary fringe. Rocks above the water table, including the capillary fringe, form the unsaturated zone; although they do contain water they are generally not completely saturated, and the water cannot be abstracted.

Groundwater comes from rain. The average annual rainfall over the UK is about 1100 millimetres, ranging from more than 2500 millimetres over highland Britain to less than 600 millimetres on the lowlands of eastern England. A significant part, almost 500 millimetres in lowland areas, evaporates, mainly in the summer. The remainder is available to infiltrate permeable rocks although where the rocks have low permeability or where they are overlain by

layers of relatively impermeable clay, part will flow over the ground as surface runoff. Water infiltrates the ground mainly in the winter and slowly moves down through the unsaturated zone,

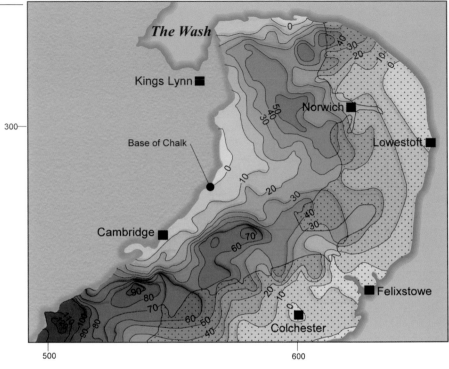

Crag and Palaeogene deposits that rest on the Chalk

G*roundwater levels in the Chalk of East Anglia (in metres above sea level).*
The hydraulic gradient is to the west, east and north from the areas of high groundwater levels located below high ground.

eventually reaching the water table and becoming groundwater.

After temporary storage in the ground, groundwater drains from springs and seepages into streams and rivers. Maximum discharges occur at the end of the winter when groundwater levels are high following the seasonal infiltration. They steadily decline throughout the summer into the autumn. The contribution that groundwater makes to the flow of rivers is called base flow and it is responsible for maintaining the flow of rivers during extended periods of dry weather, when surface runoff virtually ceases.

***P**rofile of subsurface water. The thickness of the soil layer is up to about 1 metre. Below hills the unsaturated zone can be tens of metres thick. The grain size of the rocks controls the thickness of the capillary fringe. In fine-grained rocks it can be over 10 metres while in coarse sandstones no more than several centimetres. The saturated zone can be hundreds of metres thick although most groundwater flows in the upper 200 to 300 metres.*

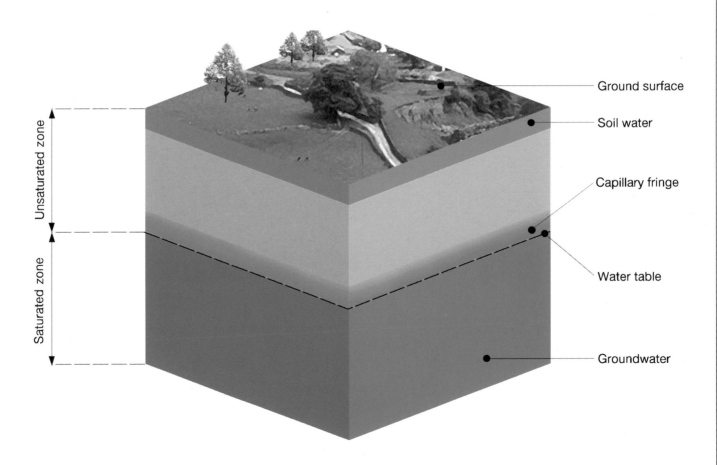

Unsaturated zone

Saturated zone

Ground surface

Soil water

Capillary fringe

Water table

Groundwater

What is groundwater?

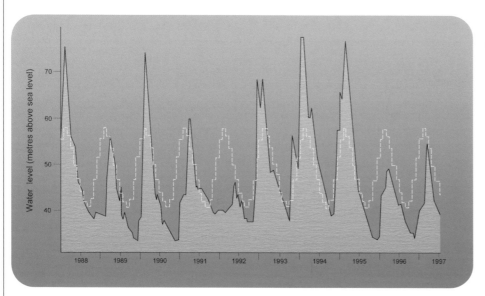

A hydrograph of the groundwater level in the Chalk measured in a well at Chilgrove in the South Downs. The water level has been measured in this well since 1836, probably the longest continuous record in the world. Over the entire period of the record the range was about 43 metres. The illustration includes two periods of low infiltration (1988–92 and 1995–97). In contrast, the high infiltration, and the consequent high water levels in the winter of 1993–94, increased the spring discharge from the Chalk, causing major flooding in Chichester. The broken line shows the mean monthly groundwater level.

A hydrograph of the River Pang in Berkshire showing the groundwater component. The river drains a Chalk catchment partly covered by clay. Groundwater discharging from the Chalk provides almost the entire flow in dry periods.

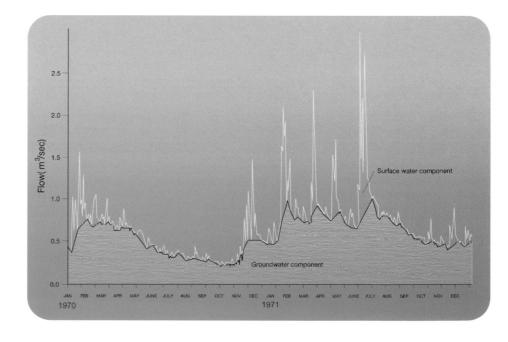

Groundwater provides about one-third of public water supplies in England and Wales, 7% in Northern Ireland and 3% in Scotland. The regional differences reflect the distribution of aquifers and the more favourable conditions for the development of surface water resources in both Northern Ireland and Scotland.

The total abstraction of groundwater in the UK, including that used by industry and agriculture, is some 2400 million m^3/year. About 85% is pumped from the two main aquifers — the Chalk and the Permo-Triassic sandstones which provide 60% and 25% respectively. Over 70% of the total public supply in south-east England is derived from groundwater, while in the Severn and Trent basins, eastern England, the Thames Valley and the Wessex region the figure is between 40 and 50%. Industry and agriculture rely on groundwater in many areas and, of course, it is still the source of supply for numerous rural communities.

*T**he Crocodile Spring at Compton Abdale in the Cotswold Hills.** The water issues from the Great Oolite Limestone and flows into the River Coln, a tributary of the Thames. The spring has never been known to fail.*

The Environment Agency controls the abstraction of groundwater in England and Wales by issuing licences which are required for all major sources of water supply. A licence is not required in Scotland or Northern Ireland, or in England and Wales if the water is used for domestic purposes.

Groundwater is relatively cheap to develop and it is generally of a very high quality. However, the cost can increase significantly if there is a need to ameliorate any undesirable impact of its development on river flows and wetlands, or provide complex water treatment to remove contaminants.

Map

Chalk

Jurassic limestones

Permo-Triassic sandstones

Devonian/Carboniferous-Older cover

SCOTLAND 3% 23

NORTHUMBRIAN 9% 33

YORKSHIRE 18% 92

NORTHERN IRELAND 42 7%

ANGLIAN 47% 326

142 NORTH WEST 15%

48%

SEVERN TRENT 409

WELSH

16 4%

SOUTH WEST 19 12%

WESSEX 158 50%

THAMES 572 41%

SOUTHERN 326 72%

Water company boundary

Percentage of total supply from groundwater 50%

Total annual groundwater abstraction in millions of cubic metres 16

*T**he use of groundwater.** Most groundwater is abstracted in central, eastern and south-eastern England.*

Aquifers: reservoirs of groundwater

***P**hotograph taken with an electron microscope of a Permian sandstone* showing the pore spaces between the grains. The porosity is about 30%.

The popular impression is that groundwater flows in subterranean channels such as those in the cave systems of the limestone country of the Peak District, South Wales and the Mendip Hills. There the drainage is entirely underground and the landform is known as karst. It is characterised by swallow holes that feed subsurface streams and caverns. But this is not the typical style of groundwater; karstic landforms are restricted to areas where hard, compact limestones outcrop and have been subjected to weathering that has dissolved the rock along lines of weakness to enlarge narrow cracks.

In contrast, most groundwater used for water supply occurs in sands and gravels, or in consolidated rocks such as sandstones and limestones; the limestones, for example the Chalk, are not so compact or hard as those in karstic areas. These rocks are both porous and permeable and form the principal groundwater reservoirs or aquifers in the UK.

An aquifer is defined as a permeable rock that stores groundwater and allows it to flow readily into a well or borehole. The water flows through the voids, or pore spaces, in the rock. The total volume of the pore space, is referred to as the porosity, and represents the total volume of water that the rock can store. This may be in the minute spaces between the grains of a sandstone, when it is referred to as intergranular porosity, or in the small cracks and fractures that are more usual in limestones and older compact rocks, which is termed fracture porosity. The pore spaces in an aquifer must be interconnected so that water can flow through the rock, in other words an aquifer must be permeable.

An aquifer's primary functions are to store and transmit water. Most groundwater in an aquifer is slowly circulating in the upper 100 to 200 metres of the saturated zone. But fresh water can penetrate to depths of more than 2 kilometres although at such depths groundwater is generally mineralised with solutes, particularly sodium and chloride, and is too saline for potable use.

Henri Darcy

Henri Darcy (1803–1858) was a French civil engineer. He investigated the flow of water through sand and found that the velocity is proportional to the hydraulic gradient. This relationship came to be known as *Darcy's law* and is the basis of quantitative hydrogeology. It is expressed as:

$$q = Ki$$

where q is the volume of flow per unit cross-sectional area, with units of velocity, i is the hydraulic gradient, which is dimensionless, and K is a constant of proportionality called the hydraulic conductivity, again with units of velocity. The hydraulic conductivity is a measure of the ability of the rock medium to transmit water and its value is different for different rocks. Values of K are high for sands and gravels and low for clays.

***T**he relationship between specific yield, specific retention and porosity* (opposite). As the grain size increases, the specific yield increases and eventually, for coarse gravels, equals the porosity.

The properties of an aquifer

The three important properties of an aquifer are its: porosity — the volume of water it holds or stores; specific yield — the volume of water it yields, when it drains naturally or is pumped; permeability — the rate that water flows through it.

In a typical sandstone the space between individual grains is very small — only about 15 microns — that is 15 millionths of a metre. However, the total volume of these spaces can amount to as much as 40% of the entire rock volume. The porosity of a limestone and compact rocks such as granite is in the form of small cracks and fractures that have been induced by earth movements and other stresses. These cracks are often enlarged in limestones by solution of the rock which enhances both the porosity and permeability. The permeability of many sandstones is also increased by fractures.

Not all the stored water represented by the porosity can be abstracted for water supply. Part, referred to as the specific retention, is retained in the aquifer against the force of gravity. The proportion that can drain freely represents the specific yield and this is the water that can be abstracted from a well or borehole or which eventually drains from the aquifer at springs. Typical values for the specific yield of a sandstone vary between 10 and 30% of the total rock volume. In most limestones, however, it amounts to only 1 or 2%. The specific yield approaches the porosity in aquifers that drain readily, for example coarse sands and gravels.

The direction of groundwater flow is indicated by the slope of the water table which is called the hydraulic gradient. The permeability of an aquifer measures the ease with which water flows through it. The velocity of the flow of water is proportional to the hydraulic gradient and a coefficient referred to as the hydraulic conductivity, which is dependant upon the interconnectivity of the pore spaces. The hydraulic conductivity of good aquifers exceeds 30 metres/day (m/d) and for many gravels 500 m/d. By way of contrast, 10^{-5} m/d is more usual for unweathered clay.

A more useful practical unit is the transmissivity. This is the product of the hydraulic conductivity and the saturated thickness of the aquifer and represents the ability of the aquifer to transmit water through its entire thickness. The unit is square metres/day (m^2/d) and values for good aquifers exceed 2000 m^2/d.

Groundwater flows very slowly. Typical speeds are between 1 metre/year and 1 metre/day, although in very fractured limestones, as in karstic regions, maximum rates are similar to those in rivers.

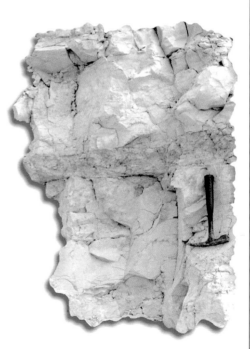

An outcrop of the Chalk showing the interconnected network of fractures that gives the aquifer its high permeability.

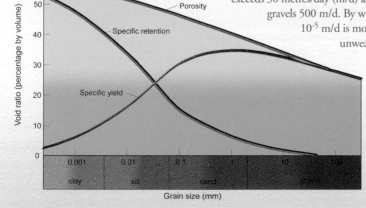

The aquifers of the UK

The principal aquifers of the UK are found in the lowlands of England. The most important are the Chalk, the Permo-Triassic sandstones, the Jurassic limestones and the Lower Greensand. They occur within the section of the geological sequence referred to as the Younger Cover, which ranges in age from the Permian to the Quaternary. Aquifers do occur in Devonian and Carboniferous strata of the underlying Older Cover but they are much harder and more compact rocks and are regarded as of secondary importance in terms of water supply. The older Silurian, Ordovician, Cambrian and Precambrian rocks generally have low permeabilities and may be regarded as an "impermeable basement" below the strata of the Older and Younger covers. However, even in these hard rocks, fractures in the upper 50 to 100 metres of the saturated zone do provide small amounts of water to individual wells and springs.

As a result of earth movements, the Jurassic to Palaeogene sequence of eastern and southern England slopes (or dips) either to the east into the North Sea Basin or to the south into the Anglo-Paris Basin. Within this broad structural pattern the subsidiary London and Hampshire basins are very significant in the hydrogeological context; each contains major aquifers.

The Chalk, which is a soft, white limestone traversed by layers of flint, underlies much of eastern and southern England. It is a unique rock because it consists of minute calcareous shells and shell fragments of plankton. These impart a high porosity to the matrix, but are so fine grained that the water contained in the pore spaces of the rock's matrix is virtually immobile, being held by capillary forces. Consequently the specific yield is low, of the order of 1%. The Chalk owes its prominent role as an aquifer to a network of fine cracks that impart a high permeability. Individual boreholes in the Chalk can yield more than 10 million litres per day (Ml/d), sufficient to provide for the needs of about 70 000 people at 150 litres per person per day.

Legend:
- Post-Carboniferous (undifferentiated)
- Chalk
- Jurassic limestones
- Permo-Triassic sandstones
- Devonian/Carboniferous-Older cover
- Impermeable basement

London Basin

Hampshire Basin

Distribution of the principal aquifers in the British Isles.

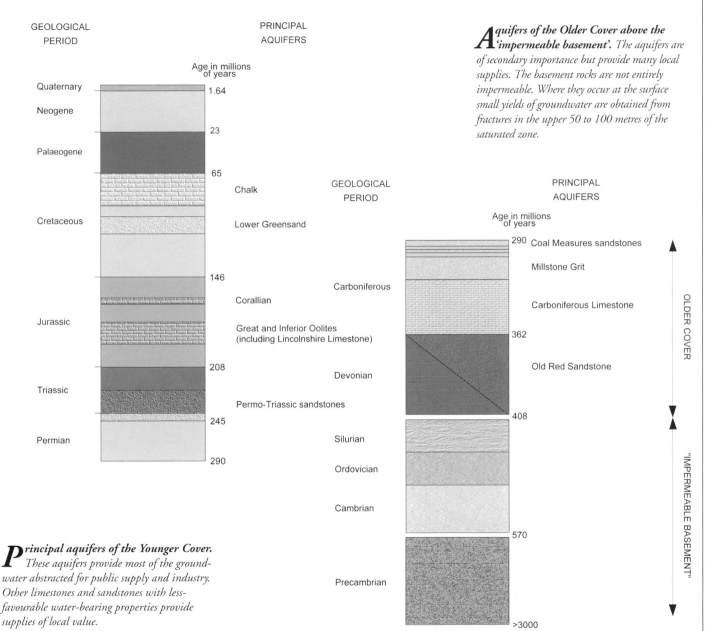

GEOLOGICAL PERIOD

PRINCIPAL AQUIFERS

Age in millions of years

Geological Period	Age (Ma)	Principal Aquifers
Quaternary	1.64	
Neogene	23	
Palaeogene	65	
Cretaceous	146	Chalk / Lower Greensand
Jurassic	208	Corallian / Great and Inferior Oolites (including Lincolnshire Limestone)
Triassic	245	Permo-Triassic sandstones
Permian	290	

***A**quifers of the Older Cover above the 'impermeable basement'. The aquifers are of secondary importance but provide many local supplies. The basement rocks are not entirely impermeable. Where they occur at the surface small yields of groundwater are obtained from fractures in the upper 50 to 100 metres of the saturated zone.*

GEOLOGICAL PERIOD

PRINCIPAL AQUIFERS

Age in millions of years

Geological Period	Age (Ma)	Principal Aquifers	
Carboniferous	290	Coal Measures sandstones / Millstone Grit / Carboniferous Limestone	OLDER COVER
Devonian	362	Old Red Sandstone	
	408		
Silurian			"IMPERMEABLE BASEMENT"
Ordovician			
Cambrian	570		
Precambrian	>3000		

***P**rincipal aquifers of the Younger Cover. These aquifers provide most of the ground-water abstracted for public supply and industry. Other limestones and sandstones with less-favourable water-bearing properties provide supplies of local value.*

The aquifers of the UK

The Permo-Triassic sandstones are mainly red sandstones that originated in a desert environment. They are found in a series of deep sedimentary basins in western England and on the eastern and western flanks of the Pennines. A deep basin lies below the Antrim basalts in Northern Ireland and small isolated basins are found in south-west Scotland. The packing of the quartz grains in the sandstones imparts a porosity of 30% and the specific yield can be as high as 20 to 25%. Much of the sandstone is a soft, compact rock that is only weakly cemented. Groundwater, therefore, can flow through the matrix but the presence of fractures enhances the permeability considerably. The sandstones are very permeable and yield a high proportion of the water that they store. Yields from large boreholes are as much as 5 to 10 Ml/d.

The Jurassic limestones are prominent aquifers in the Cotswold Hills, in eastern England and the North Yorkshire moors. They are represented by the Great and Inferior Oolites, the Lincolnshire Limestone and the Corallian limestones. They are relatively hard limestones with low specific yields but again an extensive fracture network, with fractures enlarged by

***S*ection across northern England (a)** showing the Triassic sandstones in a deep basin west of the Pennines and the aquifers of the Younger Cover in eastern England.

***S*ection across south-east England (b)** showing the Chalk in the London Basin and the South Downs.

An outcrop of the Triassic sandstones. Water flows through the sandstones between the individual grains of the rock's matrix and more rapidly along fractures.

The Chalk of eastern and southern England is the most important groundwater reservoir in the UK.

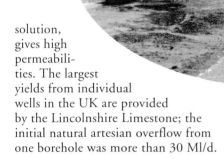

solution, gives high permeabilities. The largest yields from individual wells in the UK are provided by the Lincolnshire Limestone; the initial natural artesian overflow from one borehole was more than 30 Ml/d.

The Lower Greensand flanks the Chalk in eastern England and encircles the Weald in the south-east of the country. The aquifer is not so productive as the sandstones of the Permo-Triassic but despite this the specific yield of 10 to 20% and moderate values for permeability make it an attractive source of groundwater.

The sandstones and limestones of the Older Cover have a much longer history and in the past have been subjected to much more intensive earth movements, which are responsible for their lower porosity and permeability. Nevertheless, they do provide many local supplies. Aquifers in the Carboniferous are important in Northern England and the Central Valley of Scotland while the Old Red Sandstone is valuable in Caithness and along the Moray Firth.

Photograph taken with an electron microscope of a sample of the Chalk showing the tiny shell fragments of algae which make up most of the rock. The porosity is about 45%.

Unlike much of the rest of the world, alluvial sands and gravels are not major aquifers in the UK, although wells and boreholes are sited in these deposits in many parts of the UK and supply individual needs.

Groundwater flow

The direction of groundwater flow follows a curved path through an aquifer from areas of high water levels to areas where water levels are low; that is from below high ground, which are recharge areas, to groundwater discharge points in valleys or the sea. The direction of flow is indicated by the slope of the water table which is called the hydraulic gradient.

An aquifer that crops out (i.e. is exposed at the surface) is said to be unconfined. Because of earth movements in the past, many aquifers dip below younger strata of impermeable clay. As the thickness of the clay increases the aquifer becomes saturated throughout its entire thickness and the pressure of the water it contains increases. The water rises above the top of the aquifer and may overflow at the surface from a borehole that penetrates into the aquifer; it is said to be under artesian pressure. Such aquifers are called confined aquifers. The level to which the water rises in boreholes that penetrate into confined aquifers is known as the potentiometric surface.

Water flows through confined aquifers to discharge points some distance down-

Unconfined and confined aquifers. Aquifers are recharged by rainfall where they are unconfined. The water overflows from springs. Large volumes of water are stored below the level of these 'overflow points'. An aquifer confined by relatively impermeable strata is fully saturated. In a confined aquifer, the water pressure is greater than atmospheric pressure. Water rises in a borehole that penetrates a confined aquifer until the column of water balances the water pressure in the aquifer. Where the potentiometric surface is above the ground surface, water overflows from boreholes. Generally groundwater discharges naturally from a confined aquifer by slow upward seepage but water may be released under pressure as a spring where the confining bed is intersected by a fracture that extends into the aquifer.

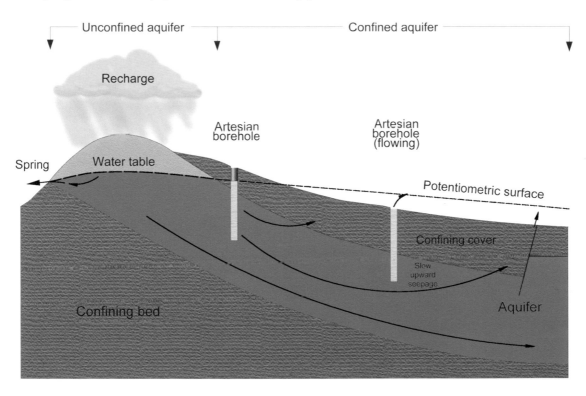

Unconfined aquifer — Confined aquifer

Recharge

Spring Water table

Artesian borehole

Artesian borehole (flowing)

Potentiometric surface

Confining cover

Slow upward seepage

Confining bed

Aquifer

Discharge

Ground surface

Water table

Cone of
depression

Drawdown in
borehole

Pumping
water level
in borehole

Groundwater flow

The drawdown of the water table around a pumping borehole to form a cone of depression. The shape and extent of the cone of depression depends upon the rate of abstraction, the duration of the abstraction and the hydraulic properties of the aquifer.

Water flows into a borehole from all directions in response to pumping and, as it is flowing through a decreasing cylindrical area, the velocity increases as it converges towards the borehole.

The age of groundwater

Water remains in rivers for a relatively short time, a matter of days or weeks. In contrast, the age of groundwater is measured in decades, or even millennia, because the water flows so slowly through the ground.

The age of groundwater can be measured from the rate of decay of radioactive elements present in the water at very low concentrations. Tritium, an isotope of hydrogen, and carbon-14 are most commonly used. Tritium and carbon-14 were formed in the atmosphere by the tests of thermonuclear bombs in the 1950s and 1960s, but carbon-14 is also formed naturally by the bombardment of nitrogen by cosmic rays.

Analysis for tritium in the late 1960s revealed that water infiltrates through the matrix of the Chalk in the unsaturated zone at a rate of about 1 metre per year. Thus where the unsaturated zone is 50 metres

gradient at a spring or possibly offshore into the sea. The isolated oases in deserts exist because groundwater is issuing from a confined aquifer which may have locally intersected the ground surface, or where the water is rising up a fracture in the overlying confining rocks. Where such outlets do not exist the water discharges from confined aquifers by slow upward seepage through the overlying clays. The velocity of flow under confined conditions is much slower than that in unconfined aquifers.

When groundwater is pumped from a borehole, the water level is lowered in the surrounding area. An hydraulic gradient is created in the aquifer which allows water to flow towards the borehole. The difference between the original water level and the pumping level is the drawdown, which is equivalent to the head of water necessary to produce a flow through the aquifer to the borehole — the greater the yield from the borehole, the greater the drawdown. The drawdown decreases with increasing distance from the borehole until a point is reached where the water level in unaffected. The surface of the pumping level is in the form of an inverted cone and is referred to as a cone of depression.

Groundwater flow

thick, water is some 50 years old when it reaches the water table. However, in such a fractured limestone some water also travels rapidly through the fractures in the unsaturated zone at velocities of the order of 50 metres per day. About 10 to 15% of the infiltration to the Chalk flows through fractures in the unsaturated zone to the water table.

Groundwater is actually a mixture of waters from many sources of different ages. The age of a particular sample is the average age of all the constituent components. In general the age of groundwater increases with depth.

Analysis for carbon-14 has shown that groundwater in the Chalk in the centre of the London Basin contains a component that is some 20 000 years old and fell as rain during the late stages of the Ice Age. Many saline groundwaters flowing at great depths are believed to be millions of years old and many may contain a component derived from the pore waters that were in the rocks when they were deposited.

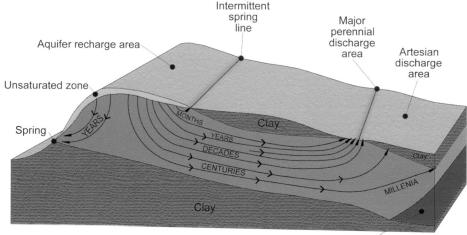

Age of groundwater. Groundwater in the upper part of the unconfined zone generally varies in age from months to years. As water penetrates to greater depths the age increases to decades, centuries or even millennia. The very saline water lying in aquifers below the zone of active freshwater circulation can be millions of years old.

Stratification of groundwaters of different ages in the Triassic sandstones of the East Midlands of England. Fresh groundwater has penetrated to a depth of about 500 m during the Holocene and late Pleistocene. Holocene water is up to 10 000 years old and Pleistocene water from 10 000 to over 30 000 years. The higher chloride value in the modern water compared to that in the Holocene reflects human contamination. (The Holocene and Pleistocene form the Quaternary.)

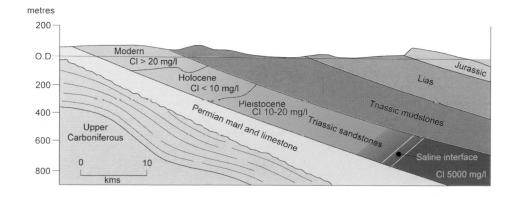

Groundwater in its natural state is generally of excellent quality. This is because rocks act as filters. Any bacterial contamination from surface sources or the soil is removed after groundwater has passed through some 30 m of saturated sand or unfissured rock; in the unsaturated zone no more than 3 metres may be necessary to purify water percolating through the zone.

Groundwater is actually a complex, generally dilute, chemical solution. The chemical composition is derived mainly from the dissolution of minerals in the soil and the rocks with which it is or has been in contact. Rainfall itself is a dilute chemical solution and contributes significant proportions of some constituents in groundwater, especially in regions with little soil cover where hard compact rocks occur at or near the surface.

As water flows through the ground the dissolution of minerals continues and the concentration of dissolved constituents tends to increase with the length of the flow path. At great depths, where the rate of flow is extremely slow, groundwater is saline, with concentrations ranging up to ten times the salinity of the sea.

Before the industrial revolution, the main risk to groundwater quality was from bacteria and viruses. Generally groundwater was free from contamination because the physical properties and the mineral constituents of rocks have a remarkable facility for purifying water. The principal action is filtration but other processes are also involved. The velocity of water flow in the small intergranular pore spaces of the unsaturated zone of a sandstone is very low. Organic compounds, bacteria and viruses tend to be retained or adsorbed on the matrix and may be degraded by microbial activity. Metals and other inorganic compounds may also be adsorbed, or diluted by mixing, or may be modified or broken down into simpler products by chemical reactions. These processes delay the transport of contaminants through an aquifer and may reduce their concentrations. However, in a fractured aquifer contaminants can rapidly pass through the unsaturated zone to the water table and the effect of the purifying processes is significantly reduced. This is particularly likely after a period of intense or prolonged rainfall. As water flows through the saturated zone, contaminants are diluted by the mixing of waters in different flow-paths, flowing at different speeds in the complex, tortuous pore passages in the aquifer.

Although the purifying capacities of rocks improve the quality of groundwater, we shall see that aquifers do not have an infinite capacity for purifying contaminated water and dilution is not a reliable remedy for pollution.

Schematic diagram of downgradient chemical changes in groundwater.
A 'hard' calcium-bicarbonate water at outcrop gradually passes into a 'soft' sodium-bicarbonate water which in turn passes into a saline sodium-chloride water.

Quality and chemical composition

Chemical changes in groundwater

The principal dissolved constituents in groundwater are calcium, magnesium, sodium, bicarbonate, sulphate and chloride.

They occur in the form of electrically charged ions. Many other minor constituents may be present, for example fluoride which helps to prevent dental caries when present in drinking water at a concentration of about 1 milligram per litre (mg/1).

As rain infiltrates through the soil it dissolves carbon dioxide, which is in the soil 'air' at a much greater concentration than in the atmosphere. The acidic solution formed reacts with carbonates in the rocks giving solutions of calcium, and to a lesser extent magnesium, bicarbonates. This is the dominant reaction in limestones and in sandstones in which the quartz grains are held together by a carbonate cement. In rocks that do not contain carbonates, as for example sands, groundwater tends to be slightly acidic and corrosive because the carbon dioxide in solution forms carbonic acid and reacts only slowly with silicate minerals. Such waters are said to be 'soft' whereas those containing calcium or magnesium bicarbonates are 'hard'. Soap easily makes a lather in 'soft' water and 'hard' water causes 'fur' in kettles.

An important source of sulphate in groundwater is the oxidation of pyrite (ferrous sulphide) which is widely distributed in sedimentary rocks. Sulphuric acid is a product of the reaction and this reacts with any carbonate present to form calcium and magnesium sulphates.

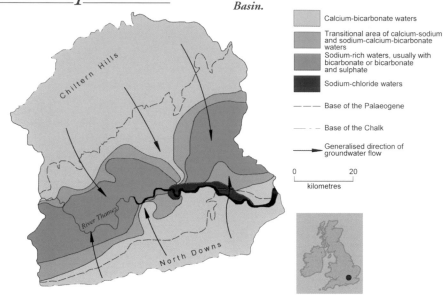

The chemical composition of groundwater in the Chalk of the London Basin.

Calcium-bicarbonate waters

Transitional area of calcium-sodium and sodium-calcium-bicarbonate waters

Sodium-rich waters, usually with bicarbonate or bicarbonate and sulphate

Sodium-chloride waters

----- Base of the Palaeogene

—·—·— Base of the Chalk

⟶ Generalised direction of groundwater flow

0   20
kilometres

The reaction may be promoted by sulphur-oxidising bacteria.

Most of the chloride found in groundwaters that are actively circulating at relatively shallow depths is derived from rain or, near coastlines, from sea spray.

The dominant chemical reaction in aquifers where they outcrop is the solution of minerals in the aquifer's matrix. The water in limestones and calcareous sandstones contains calcium and magnesium balanced with bicarbonate and sulphate. As these groundwaters flow down the hydraulic gradient below confining clays they are modified by ion exchange, the calcium and magnesium in the water being replaced by sodium from minerals in the aquifer's matrix. The water is thereby converted from a 'hard' water to a 'soft' sodium bicarbonate or sodium sulphate water.

Groundwater in aquifers where they outcrop contains dissolved oxygen. As the water flows downgradient this decreases as organic matter and ferrous iron in the aquifer's matrix are oxidised. When the oxygen has been used up, other ions, such as nitrate and sulphate, provide oxygen. These ions are converted to nitrogen and sulphide by reactions promoted mainly by anaerobic bacteria. A final stage in some deep aquifers is the reduction of carbon dioxide to methane.

The very saline groundwaters found at depths below the actively circulating zone, are formed by the gradual solution of soluble constituents in aquifers and also by the modification, concentration and migration of the sea water that was in many rocks when they formed. Some hydrogeologists believe some groundwaters have been concentrated by the filtering action of clays which act as semi-permeable membranes.

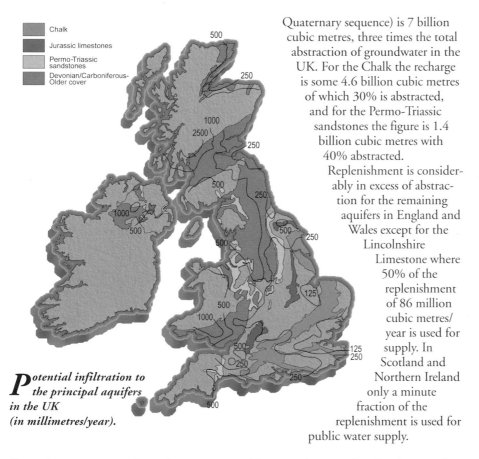

Chalk

Jurassic limestones

Permo-Triassic sandstones

Devonian/Carboniferous-Older cover

Potential infiltration to the principal aquifers in the UK (in millimetres/year).

Quaternary sequence) is 7 billion cubic metres, three times the total abstraction of groundwater in the UK. For the Chalk the recharge is some 4.6 billion cubic metres of which 30% is abstracted, and for the Permo-Triassic sandstones the figure is 1.4 billion cubic metres with 40% abstracted.

Replenishment is considerably in excess of abstraction for the remaining aquifers in England and Wales except for the Lincolnshire Limestone where 50% of the replenishment of 86 million cubic metres/year is used for supply. In Scotland and Northern Ireland only a minute fraction of the replenishment is used for public water supply.

The Chalk crops out over more than 20 000 square kilometres, rather more than twice that of the Permo-Triassic sandstones. The top 20 metres alone of the unconfined saturated zones of these two aquifers contain 4000 and 36 000 million cubic metres of water respectively. The much larger figure for the sandstones, despite the smaller outcrop, is because the specific yield is much larger. A volume of the sandstone contains about 20 times as much drainable water as the same volume of the Chalk. If the volume of water in the confined zones is included, the figures for total storage are even larger. Although not all this water is available where it is required, and in some areas the permeability may not be favourable for large-scale development, the figures indicate the scale of groundwater storage in aquifers. A conservative estimate indicates that 20 times as much water is stored in the upper 20 metres of the two main aquifers as in all the surface reservoirs in the UK.

Groundwater resources depend upon rainfall and factors such as evaporation and the size of an aquifer's outcrop. Where the main aquifers crop out in the lowlands of England the potential infiltration is less than 500 mm/year and in the extreme east less than 150 mm/year.

The average annual replenishment, or recharge, to the main aquifers of the Younger Cover (the Permian to

However, the annual replenishment of the resources is only part of the story. Aquifers store large volumes of water in the saturated zone, far in excess of that in surface reservoirs which is about 2500 million cubic metres. Springs are where groundwater overflows from aquifers but, as in surface reservoirs, water is stored in aquifers below the overflow levels. This storage remains available for development after springs have stopped flowing.

By providing the base flow component of river flow, groundwater is also the source of water abstracted at river intakes for public supply and other uses during dry periods. Because of the importance of maintaining river flows, several major schemes in England have been designed to pump groundwater into rivers in dry periods and thereby make water continuously available for abstraction at water supply intakes as well as protecting the aquatic environment.

The natural infiltration to an aquifer can be supplemented by a process called artificial recharge. The object is to make use of

Groundwater resources

the large storage capacity of aquifers to store water that is surplus to requirements, for use when supplies are less plentiful. Water may be recharged through basins or boreholes, or simply spread over the ground in ditches or by controlled flooding.

Artificial recharge has been used only to a limited extent in the UK. The Chalk

and overlying Palaeogene sands are being recharged in the London Basin with treated river water. During the 1960s and 1970s extensive field trials demonstrated that recharge of the Permo-Triassic sandstones and the Lower Greensand through basins and boreholes should present few problems but, so far, the technique has not been applied in these aquifers.

***T**riassic sandstones aquifer in Shropshire. Groundwater from the Triassic sandstones, as well as water from Lake*

Vyrnwy and Llyn Clywedog, is used to regulate the flow of the River Severn and thereby supply water for many communities.

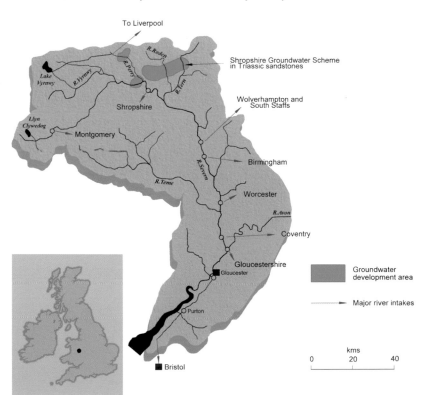

Shropshire groundwater scheme

The River Severn provides water for many communities in the West Midlands between Shrewsbury and Bristol. During the summer the river level may be insufficient to meet these needs while at the same time preserving the river's environment. When this occurs the flow is increased by releasing water stored in the Llyn Clywedog and Lake Vyrnwy reservoirs in the headwaters of the river in central Wales. However, in dry years, such as 1976, 1989 and 1995, the capacity of the reservoirs is insufficient to provide all the water required to maintain the river at an adequate level. In these exceptional years of drought another reservoir is also used to augment the flow of the river — the Triassic sandstones aquifer of north Shropshire.

Groundwater is pumped from boreholes in the sandstones and discharged through pipelines into the River Severn or its tributaries. When the scheme is fully developed, pumping will be required to some extent about one year in three, but for not more than 100 days even in a very dry year. The total abstraction that will ultimately be permitted from the sandstones will be 330 Ml/d, which will allow an increase in abstraction from the River Severn of about 225 Ml/d. The difference between the two figures is because groundwater would have entered the river naturally if pumping had not taken place, but is intercepted by the cones of depression that form around the boreholes.

The Shropshire Scheme is typical of many schemes that have been developed over the last 20 years to augment river

Hills, passing below London and rising to the surface again in the North Downs. They form a classic confined aquifer.

Groundwater was first developed from the aquifers below London in the eighteenth century. Over the next 200 years many boreholes were drilled. The water level gradually fell and saline water from the tidal River Thames intruded into the

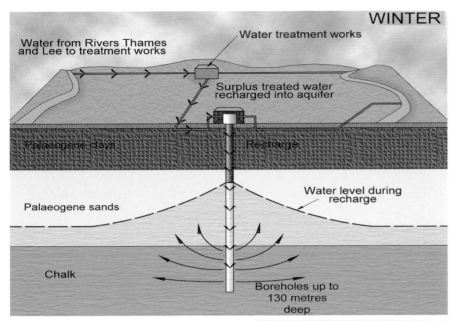

*A*rtificial recharge of the Chalk in the Lee Valley. *Surplus treated water is stored in the aquifer until it is needed. Water abstracted from boreholes sited along the New River is discharged into the river to maintain the flow, before being piped from the reservoir at Stoke Newington to the treatment works.*

flows and provide continuing water supplies and/or environmental benefits during droughts. They make use of groundwater storage that already exists and they can be developed in stages to meet the needs as they arise, so that capital does not have to be spent before it is necessary. The Shropshire Scheme is being developed in eight stages.

The reservoir under London

London is built on a thick layer of clay appropriately called the London Clay. Below the clay, the Chalk and Palaeogene sands form a major groundwater reservoir. They lie in a saucer-shaped depression extending from outcrops in the Chiltern

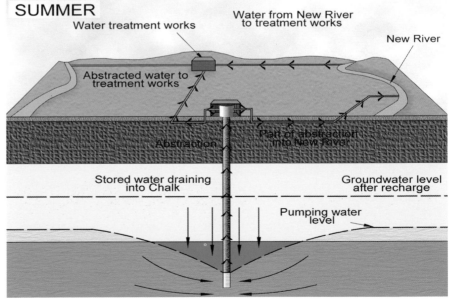

Groundwater resources

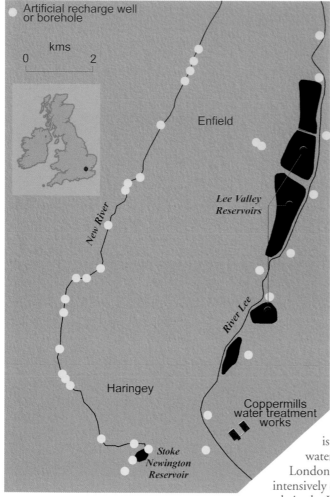

Sites of artificial recharge boreholes and wells in the Lee Valley.

aquifers where they crop out along the lower reaches of the river. These consequences were naturally seen as undesirable, but it is indisputable that the availability of a convenient source of water below London made a significant contribution to the economic development of the city in the nineteenth and early twentieth centuries. Between 1800 and 1965 the aquifers in the central part of the London Basin provided some 5700 million cubic metres of water. The groundwater storage was used very effectively.

As explained elsewhere, a change in the pattern of water use is leading to a recovery of water levels below central London but the Chalk is still intensively exploited for public water supply in the Lee Valley, where 70 M l/d are abstracted.

In the Lee Valley, the void space in the aquifers, made available by the fall in water level, is being replenished by artificial recharge. This began over 40 years ago. Thames Water increased the scale of the operation and now recharge water through 36 wells and boreholes. In the winter, when the demand for water is lower, surplus surface water from the rivers Thames and Lee is treated and recharged into the Chalk. During hot dry summers, times of high demand for water, the stored water is pumped from the aquifers, treated once again and then distributed. Part of the water from the boreholes and wells is pumped into the New River which carries it to a reservoir at Stoke Newington. It is then piped to the treatment works. The flow in the river is thereby maintained, preserving this historical aqueduct, built in 1613, to bring groundwater from springs in Hertfordshire to the heart of London.

Artificial recharge now provides Londoners with 100 million litres of water per day at times of drought.

Hot and saline waters

The seventeenth and eighteenth centuries saw fashionable society indulging in the re-emergence of an old pastime of 'taking the waters'. The practice continued into the nineteenth century but declined after that in the UK, although remaining popular in Europe. 'Taking the waters' involved the luxury of bathing in and/or drinking the mineral or thermal waters of spa towns such as Bath, Buxton and Cheltenham. The waters were believed to be good for rheumatism, respiratory illnesses, skin conditions and digestive disorders.

Most of the mineral waters used for therapeutic purposes have a dissolved solute

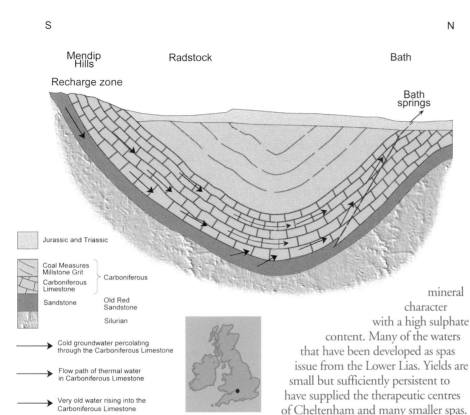

S   N

Mendip Hills Radstock   Bath

Recharge zone

Bath springs

Legend:
- Jurassic and Triassic
- Coal Measures / Millstone Grit — Carboniferous
- Carboniferous Limestone — Carboniferous
- Sandstone — Old Red Sandstone
- Silurian

→ Cold groundwater percolating through the Carboniferous Limestone

→ Flow path of thermal water in Carboniferous Limestone

→ Very old water rising into the Carboniferous Limestone

The origin of the thermal springs at Bath. Groundwater flows through the Carboniferous Limestone in a huge siphon extending from the Mendip Hills. It descends to depths of about 2 km before rising up fractures to discharge as springs at Bath, some 15 km to the north. As it flows through the rocks it becomes hotter and when it flows from the springs the temperature is 46°C. The water is probably several thousand years old but it includes a very much older component derived from the underlying Old Red Sandstone.

content of more than 1000 milligrams per litre, in other words they taste salty and some are very salty, including those at Harrogate and Leamington Spa where the total dissolved solute contents are about 16 000 milligrams per litre. Most of the waters are not thermal waters. Many are associated with clays and derive their mineral content from soluble minerals that occur in these deposits. Groundwaters in rock formations such as the London Clay, the Kimmeridge Clay, the Oxford Clay and the Lower Lias are almost invariably of a mineral character with a high sulphate content. Many of the waters that have been developed as spas issue from the Lower Lias. Yields are small but sufficiently persistent to have supplied the therapeutic centres of Cheltenham and many smaller spas. The salt deposits of the Triassic rocks are a further important source of mineral water and have been developed at Droitwich and Leamington Spa.

Thermal waters are found as natural springs only in the Peak District of Derbyshire and at Bath, Bristol and Taff's Well, in South Wales. They are warm rather than hot waters. The maximum temperature recorded is 46°C at Bath. These waters have all been heated as they circulated to considerable depths in fractures in the the Carboniferous Limestone, although they do not all issue from this rock. Only the thermal waters issuing at Bath and Bristol are mineral waters and they contain relatively low total dissolved solutes.

In the UK the temperature below the ground increases with depth at an average rate of 25°C per kilometre but in places it exceeds 30°C per kilometre. As a consequence hot groundwaters in permeable rocks at depths of some $1\frac{1}{2}$ to 3 kilometres represent a source of thermal energy. Advantage of this has only been taken at Southampton where brines at a temperature of 75°C are pumped from Triassic sandstones at a depth of 1.7 kilometres and used to heat buildings in the centre of the city.

There are signs that 'taking the waters' is making a comeback in the UK. A number of towns are planning to reopen spa baths. There seems to be little doubt that wallowing in warm saline water makes one feel better.

Groundwater resources

*T*he Great Roman Bath at Bath.
The bath is filled by thermal water from the King's Spring, one of the three thermal springs in Bath.

Bottled water — a matter of taste

Supermarkets' shelves now carry an impressive selection of bottled waters. This is a recent phenomenon and clearly reflects public concern about the quality of tap water. The increase in demand for bottled water has been attributed to better taste, or great purity, or a real or perceived health benefit. Whatever the reason over 500 million litres are sold each year in the UK.

Almost all bottled waters are groundwaters. They are collected from springs or boreholes selected because the sites are generally in upland areas remote from sources of pollution, and they provide a water which does not contain undesirable chemicals such as excessive nitrate. Many have very low concentrations of dissolved constituents, and some are carbonated artificially.

Bottled waters are 'natural waters'; they are bottled from the source after only limited treatment, mainly filtration if that is necessary. Consequently they have not been sterilised. They can contain bacteria, although most would be harmless.

In contrast, public water supplies provided from groundwater sources have been sterilised before distribution and they meet the stringent drinking water standards of the European Union and the World Health Organisation.

Bottled water is 500 to 1000 times more expensive than tap water and as sold in restaurants can exceed the cost of petrol or wine sold by the carafe.

Climate change

A change of climate resulting from the increasing amounts of the 'greenhouse gases' in the atmosphere, particularly carbon dioxide, methane, nitrous oxide, tropospheric ozone and chlorofluorocarbons, is now more widely accepted. Much uncertainty surrounds the detailed effects in the UK but there is a consensus that by 2050 the average temperature will be 1.6° C higher than the average for the period 1961–90. The total annual rainfall is predicted to increase by 10% but summer rainfall is expected to decline over most of England and Wales. The summers would tend to be more prolonged, curtailing the winter recharge season. Droughts would be more common and dry winters would be of much greater significance. Conditions similar to the dry period of 1988–92 may be more frequent.

The effect of climate change on groundwater resources depends upon any change in the volume and distribution of infiltration. If drier warmer summers lead to the seasonal deficits in the moisture content of soils extending into the autumn, the winter recharge season for aquifers would be shortened. This could be compensated, at least to some extent, by an increase in winter rainfall. Lower rainfall in the spring would have an effect on groundwater levels, spring flows and the volume of base flow in rivers during the subsequent summer. Aquifers are recharged more effectively by prolonged steady rain, which continues into the spring, rather than short periods of intense rainfall.

An important outcome of climate change is likely to be that groundwater storage will assume increasing importance. It will have to be developed in conjunction with surface water within more complex regional water-resource management systems that incorporate seasonal use of groundwater and artificial recharge, as well as the flexible transfer of water between regions to counter uneven distribution of the basic resource — rain.

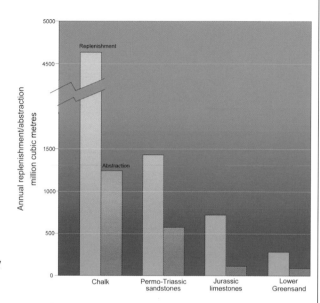

*C*omparison of replenishment and abstraction of groundwater for the principal aquifers of the UK.

*I*ncreasing river flow with groundwater.
Groundwater is pumped from boreholes into some rivers during extended dry periods to maintain adequate flows in the rivers. The boreholes are sited some distance from the rivers and the water abstracted is taken from groundwater storage. In the short-term the abstraction does not affect the flow of the rivers.

Groundwater is piped to the river to augment the flow

Groundwater level

Groundwater flow-lines

Groundwater development

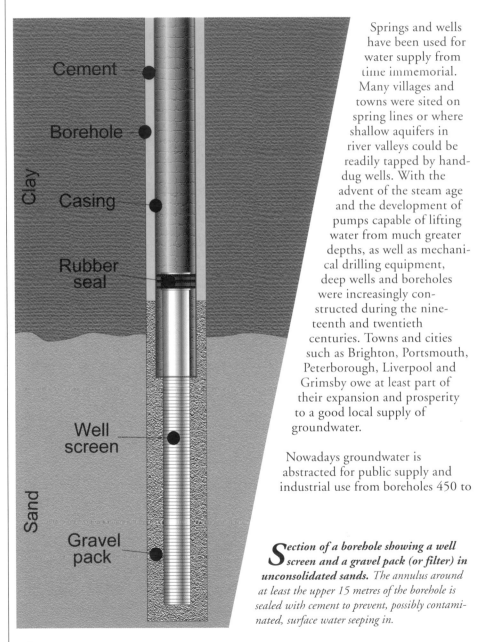

Cement

Borehole

Clay

Casing

Rubber seal

Well screen

Sand

Gravel pack

Section of a borehole showing a well screen and a gravel pack (or filter) in unconsolidated sands. The annulus around at least the upper 15 metres of the borehole is sealed with cement to prevent, possibly contaminated, surface water seeping in.

Springs and wells have been used for water supply from time immemorial. Many villages and towns were sited on spring lines or where shallow aquifers in river valleys could be readily tapped by hand-dug wells. With the advent of the steam age and the development of pumps capable of lifting water from much greater depths, as well as mechanical drilling equipment, deep wells and boreholes were increasingly constructed during the nineteenth and twentieth centuries. Towns and cities such as Brighton, Portsmouth, Peterborough, Liverpool and Grimsby owe at least part of their expansion and prosperity to a good local supply of groundwater.

Nowadays groundwater is abstracted for public supply and industrial use from boreholes 450 to 900 millimetres in diameter and generally up to 100 metres deep. If the aquifer consists of sands that could collapse into the borehole, the borehole is lined with a slotted steel or plastic pipe (a well screen) that may be surrounded by a gravel filter (or gravel pack). The water is pumped to the surface with electrically driven pumps referred to as electric-submersibles because both the pump and the motor are installed in the borehole below the water table. Such boreholes yield as much as 100 litres/second.

Many farms, households and communities in rural areas still obtain their water supply from shallow wells or small-diameter boreholes. In these situations groundwater is the only practical means of supply. Because such sources are relatively shallow and often near habitation, they are vulnerable to contamination. Care is necessary to ensure that the annulus between a well or borehole and the rock strata is well cemented to a depth of about 15 metres to prevent the ingress of surface drainage or possibly farm effluents.

In the past, tunnels or adits were driven horizontally from large-diameter wells to tap a larger volume of an aquifer. This practice has been discontinued partly because of the cost but mainly because the required yield could be obtained more effectively by drilling more boreholes. However, in the Chalk of south-east England there are many kilometres of water adits still in use; in the Lee and Darent valleys, east of London, there are 18 kilometres and on the Isle of Thanet, in Kent, 14 kilometres.

If groundwater is abstracted from an aquifer at rates that exceed the average long-term replenishment from rainfall, water levels steadily decline and the yield of water will eventually decrease. The long-term decline of levels is undesirable but must not be confused with short-term falls during periods of drought. The management of groundwater resources is concerned with the optimum use of the water stored in aquifers, storage that has very little value unless it is put to good use. An aquifer is a reservoir and to use the storage capacity effectively it must be accepted that water levels will fall as short-term demands for water are met. Water levels recover quickly when rainfall patterns are re-established.

An advantage of groundwater as a source of water is that it is not affected by abnormal seasonal weather as much as surface water sources. Groundwater supplies in major aquifers are little affected by one or even two dry winters. During droughts groundwater levels are often said to be 'very low', the mental link being with very low levels in surface reservoirs. But 'very low groundwater levels' in the Permo-Triassic sandstones are generally no more than a metre below the mean, while the thickness of the aquifer is some 200 metres or more. In a fractured aquifer, such as the Chalk, the difference between drought water levels and the mean level is greater, ranging up to possibly 7 or 8 metres below areas of high ground, although less below low ground, in an aquifer at least 50 metres thick. Yields from boreholes do decline in the summer and autumn following dry winters, but aquifers, unlike surface reservoirs, do not dry up, although they do stop overflowing from springs. Aquifers can also be developed gradually, in stages as required, and often where the water is needed; long pipelines are not necessary.

Development of groundwater must ensure a sustainable balance between the proportion of the natural recharge abstracted for supply and the amount left to flow naturally from an aquifer to protect the aquatic environment, particularly river flows. At times of low river flows, problems of water quality increase, putting aquatic life at risk. Thus, the sustainable yield of an aquifer must allow for both the consumptive and environmental uses of groundwater.

***G**roundwater flowing from a fracture in the Chalk into a tunnel (or adit) driven from a well in the Lee Valley.*

Groundwater development

The origin of the Bedhampton and Havant Springs. Groundwater flow in the Chalk aquifer is focused on a fractured zone in the Chalk which allows the water to pass below the Chichester Syncline.

Chalk springs supply Portsmouth

Portsmouth obtains its water supply from a closely defined group of 28 springs which issue from the Chalk between Bedhampton and Havant, some 10 kilometres to the north-east of the city. About 60 Ml are abstracted each day. It is the largest public water supply from a spring source in the UK. The flow of the springs actually varies between about 65 and 165 Ml/d with an average flow of about 100 Ml/d.

The springs are draining rainfall that infiltrates into almost 100 square kilometres of the Chalk's outcrop at the western end of the South Downs. Such a large flow of groundwater emerging from so small an area is a direct consequence of the geology. Just to the north of Bedhampton and Havant, the Chalk is overlain by Palaeogene deposits. Both formations have been folded into a syncline that takes the top of the Chalk to a depth of over 60 metres below sea level, and which acts as a barrier to the southward flow of groundwater. However, near the springs the syncline is not so deep and the Chalk is also very fractured. The flow of groundwater is focused on this fractured zone which provides channels through the Chalk allowing the water to pass under the syncline and re-emerge at the springs on the south side.

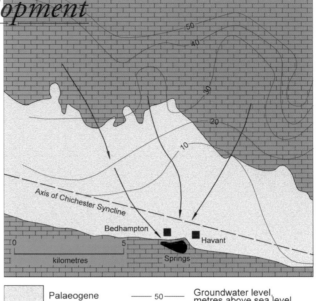

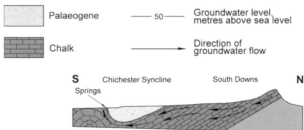

Palaeogene	—— 50 ——	Groundwater level, metres above sea level
Chalk	⟶	Direction of groundwater flow

Two sources of water supply for Peterborough

Peterborough takes a major part of its water supply from the Lincolnshire Limestone. Up to 40 Ml/d are pumped to the city from this prolific aquifer with individual boreholes yielding more than 15 Ml/d.

Over much of the Fenland north of Peterborough the water pressure in the aquifer is still high enough for water to overflow at the surface. However, during periods of drought the yield declines and the rivers that depend on springs issuing from the aquifer can also dry up. When this occurs the supply to the city is augmented with surface water from Rutland Water. Water released from the reservoir into the River Gwash is also pumped into the River West Glen to maintain the flow in this river, which normally depends upon limestone springs for its supply.

In this manner a balance is struck between public water supply and the needs of the aquatic environment.

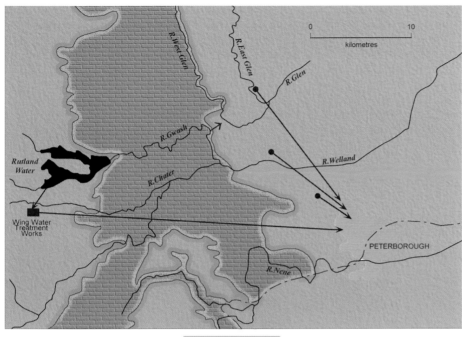

Transfer point for river augmentation

Groundwater pumping station for public supply

Southern limit of Lincolnshire Limestone

Outcrop of the Lincolnshire Limestone

***The two sources of water for Peterborough.** The city obtains its water supply from the Lincolnshire Limestone aquifer. At times of drought this source is augmented with water from Rutland Water.*

More recently, patterns of groundwater use in cities have changed. Industrial activity has declined and many private boreholes have become disused as preference switched to public water supplies. A further factor was a decline in the quality of groundwater below cities because of surface contamination and in some cases saline intrusion from the sea or tidal rivers. Consequently water levels have begun to rise towards levels prevailing at the beginning of the nineteenth century. This has led to fears about the flooding of basements and tunnels, and damage to the foundations of buildings. In Liverpool pumping has had to be increased to provide adequate drainage for a railway tunnel and basements have been flooded in Birmingham. Below London, the water level in the Chalk is rising at a rate of up to 3 metres/year. The level is still some 30 to 40 metres below ground level but, nevertheless, the rate of rise is giving cause for concern. The foundations of the new British Library have been modified because higher water levels may occur in the future, and affect the stability of the building. The tunnels of the London Underground and deep telecommunication cable ducts are also particularly at risk.

Solution of the problem requires abstraction of groundwater from boreholes to control the rise of the levels, either locally around specific buildings at risk, or regionally by water companies using at least part of the water for public supply after appropriate treatment.

Rising groundwater levels under cities

In the nineteenth and early part of the twentieth centuries large volumes of groundwater were pumped from aquifers below cities, including London, Birmingham and Liverpool. Considerable falls in groundwater levels resulted. In London many industries, businesses and offices, for example the Bank of England and the Savoy Hotel, had boreholes or wells into the Chalk. The groundwater level below central London had fallen to almost 90 m below ground level by the mid-1960s.

29

Low river flows and wetlands

Most rivers derive their flows from both surface runoff and groundwater discharge. Surface runoff from impermeable ground occurs mainly in winter, is intermittent and of relatively short duration. In summer and autumn, when river flows are low, much of the base flow is groundwater.

Rivers draining areas that consist entirely of permeable rocks (e.g. the chalk downlands of southern England) obtain virtually all their water from aquifers. Flows are at a maximum at the end of winter or in early spring, when groundwater levels are high, and decline progressively from late spring to autumn. As the water table falls in the Chalk aquifer, streams may dry up as the point of discharge of groundwater moves downstream. Such streams, referred to as winterbournes (or simply bournes), may remain dry for extended periods during droughts such as those experienced in 1933/34, 1975/76, and 1988 – 1992 and 1995 – 1997.

Wetlands are formed in valley floors by flows of groundwater from springs and seepages. Wetland soils are saturated periodically and plants adapt to saturated conditions, resulting in habitats which depend on an excess of water for much of the year. These environments generally occur on, or at the margins of, floodplains where aquifers are overlain by superficial deposits (such as alluvium or glacial deposits) or where organic silts and peats have accumulated. Preservation of wetland habitats and the wildlife they support thus depends in

Section through Redgrave and Lopham Fen. *The section shows the natural groundwater flow situation. Abstraction of groundwater from boreholes in the Chalk aquifer reverses the flow direction.*

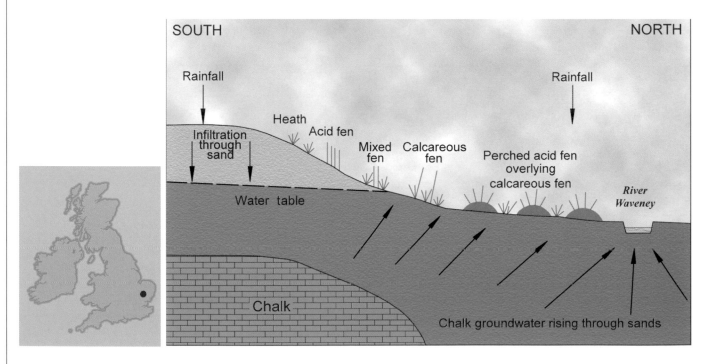

many areas (e.g. eastern England) on maintaining groundwater flows from natural outlets.

Effective management of groundwater involves a balance between abstraction for water supply and the maintenance of adequate river flows. The deleterious effect of excessive groundwater abstraction has been recognised since the early 1960s, after the drought of 1959 focused attention on the problem. One solution involves conjunctive use of groundwater with surface runoff to meet projected demand for water supply and to maintain residual flows in rivers at acceptable levels. Basically the object has been to optimise the use of water resources by abstracting surface water when available in preference to groundwater, and drawing on groundwater reserves at other times. In many situations groundwater is pumped into rivers during extended periods of dry weather to maintain flows both to preserve the aquatic environment and, if necessary, provide for the abstraction of water downstream for water supply. Nevertheless, the flow of a number of rivers continues to give cause for concern because of low base flows at certain times of the year.

While abstraction of groundwater has been identified as an important factor in relation to low flows, the situation is complicated by other influences such as variability in rainfall intensity and rate of evaporation, changes in land use (e.g. by agriculture, and by urbanisation and afforestation), land drainage, and the

*H*opton Fen in East Anglia. *A wetland maintained by groundwater.*

control of discharges of effluents (domestic and industrial) and cooling water.

Revitalising a wetland

Redgrave and Lopham Fen is a spring-fed wetland in the headwaters of the River Waveney in East Anglia. It is designated as a wetland of international importance and is likely to become a Special Area of Conservation under legislation of the European Union. It covers some 125 hectares and is the largest fen of its type in lowland England.

Until the late 1950s, groundwater rose under artesian pressure into the fen from the underlying Chalk. The water issued from springs and seepages around the edge of the fen and within the peat subsoil, and flowed over the surface even during the summer. This kept the peat waterlogged with a lime-rich water, low in nutrients. An acid wet heath was also

maintained by more-acidic rainfall at the higher margins of the fen.

In the late 1950s, two boreholes were drilled close to the fen to provide public water supplies. As a consequence of the pumping, the upward and lateral movement of Chalk groundwater was replaced by downward movement of rainwater. The fen began to dry out and

31

Low river flows and wetlands

the quality of the fauna and flora deteriorated; in particular the number of species preferring calcareous conditions declined.

Recently, steps have been taken to encourage a recovery of the ecology. The boreholes will be relocated at a site some distance from the fen, the restored flow of water through the fen will be managed so that flood-flows and water levels are controlled with the aid of a small sluice, extensive scrub clearance will be undertaken and traditional fen management practices re-introduced.

These changes, the result of cooperation between the Environment Agency, Essex and Suffolk Water, English Nature and the Suffolk Wildlife Trust, will successfully balance the need for public water supply with concern for the survival of an important wetland.

Preserving the River Darent

The River Darent rises from springs in the Chalk and Lower Greensand west of Sevenoaks, and flows over the Chalk to discharge into the Thames at Dartford. Groundwater abstraction from public supply boreholes in both the Lower Greensand and the Chalk is at the expense of the springs, and hence the river. During dry periods the flow is

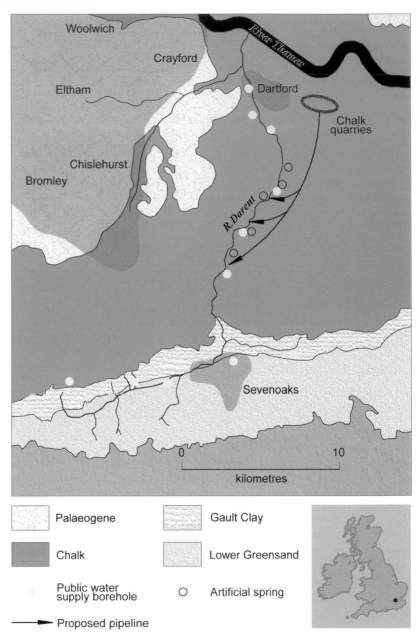

Key:

Palaeogene

Chalk

Gault Clay

Lower Greensand

● Public water supply borehole

○ Artificial spring

→ Proposed pipeline

Preserving the River Darent.
The elements of the scheme.

32

unacceptably low and for long periods the lower reaches have been completely dry. A number of steps have been taken recently by Thames Water and the Environment Agency to remedy this. The object is to maintain sufficient flow in the river to sustain natural fisheries, particularly Brown Trout.

Thames Water is now developing the resources of the River Thames in conjunction with the groundwater in the Chalk and Lower Greensand to reduce the impact of groundwater abstraction on the Darent. Surface water from the Thames will be used during the winter thereby allowing maximum natural replenishment of groundwater storage. Abstraction of groundwater for public supply from six boreholes in the Chalk adjacent to the river and from boreholes in the Lower Greensand will be reduced

by 30%. During severe droughts the use of groundwater will have to be increased but, because the boreholes will be used to a lesser extent overall, groundwater levels will be higher and the impact on the river will be less in the short term.

Shallow boreholes have been drilled into the Chalk near the river to act as artificial springs, enabling groundwater to be pumped into the river at times of dry weather. Furthermore, groundwater from the Chalk that currently drains into large quarries near Dartford may be recirculated by a pipeline to discharge points in the middle reaches of the river.

These comprehensive measures should maintain the flow of the Darent and at the same time make the best use of both groundwater and surface resources. It is an example of how, by innovative man-

agement, groundwater can provide both a water supply and meet obligations to maintain the river environment.

D*ry winters produce dry bournes.* *Winterbournes drain groundwater from the Chalk and they dry up naturally in the summer and autumn when the water table falls below the bed of the stream. After extremely dry winters they are dry for much longer periods. This occurred following the dry winters of 1995/6 and 1996/7.*

Sea-water intrusion

Chalk

Permo-Triassic sandstones

● Locations affected by sea-water intrusion

WEST HARTLEPOOL

HULL
GRIMSBY

MERSEY

IPSWICH
FELIXSTOWE
MANNINGTREE

THAMES

BRIGHTON

***M**ain areas of sea-water intrusion. Except for West Hartlepool, the aquifers affected are the Chalk and Permo-Triassic sandstones. At West Hartlepool the aquifer affected is the Permian Magnesian Limestone.*

Where aquifers form a coastline, a natural gradient exists towards the coast and groundwater discharges into the sea. Because sea water is slightly heavier than fresh water, it intrudes into aquifers in coastal areas forming a saline wedge below the fresh water. The boundary, or interface, between the two is in a state of dynamic equilibrium, moving with the seasonal variations of the water table and daily tidal fluctuations. These movements mean the interface is actually a transition zone of mixed salinity.

The theoretical interface actually occurs at a depth below sea level that is 40 times the height of fresh water above sea level; this relationship is called the Ghyben–Herzberg relation, after the two European scientists who independently recognised it at the turn of the century. In practise geological variability makes the relationship more complex.

When groundwater is pumped from a coastal aquifer the fresh-water level is lowered and the sea intrudes further into the aquifer.

With excessive pumping the natural hydraulic gradient towards the sea may be reversed and the intrusion can then extend to the pumping borehole which becomes saline.

Saline intrusion has occurred in Britain at a limited number of locations where the Chalk and Permo-Triassic sandstones have been extensively exploited. The cause is usually industrial abstraction concentrated in coastal areas of large towns. The volume of water pumped is generally limited by the chloride concentration and, if the increase in salinity cannot be controlled, the boreholes are eventually abandoned. To this extent the problem is self-correcting.

In many sandstones, where the flow is mainly intergranular, saline intrusion moves slowly inland on a broad front, but in fractured aquifers, such as the Chalk, intrusion can be rapid along individual fractures and extend inland for considerable distances.

To control saline intrusion, a seaward hydraulic gradient should be maintained and a proportion of the natural fresh-water recharge allowed to flow into the sea. The management of a coastal aquifer is actually concerned with deciding upon an acceptable ultimate landward extent of the saline water and calculating the amount of fresh-water discharge necessary to keep it in that position.

The risk of saline intrusion clearly limits the extent to which a coastal aquifer can be developed for water supply but the proportion of the infiltration that can be used can be increased by skilful management.

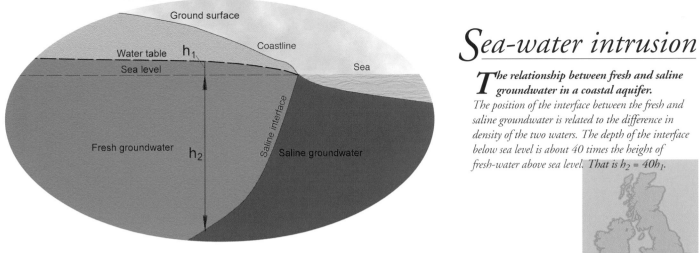

The relationship between fresh and saline groundwater in a coastal aquifer. _The position of the interface between the fresh and saline groundwater is related to the difference in density of the two waters. The depth of the interface below sea level is about 40 times the height of fresh-water above sea level. That is $h_2 = 40h_1$._

Controlling the sea

Various methods have been advocated for the control of saline intrusion but the pragmatic and cheapest solution is to reduce and/or rearrange the pattern of boreholes abstracting groundwater. This approach has been very successfully applied near Brighton where the Chalk is affected by intrusion, in this case because of abstraction for public supply. The policy adopted is that in the winter, when fresh-water flow to the sea is large, boreholes near the sea are used to provide most of the supply and inland boreholes are rested. This situation is reversed in the summer when the flow of fresh water to the sea is much reduced and the potential for intrusion thereby increased.

Along the south bank of the Humber, where the aquifer in question is again the Chalk, a similar problem has been overcome by using groundwater from the aquifer and surface water from the rivers Trent and Ancholme, in conjunction. Each source is used at different times of the year according to its availability.

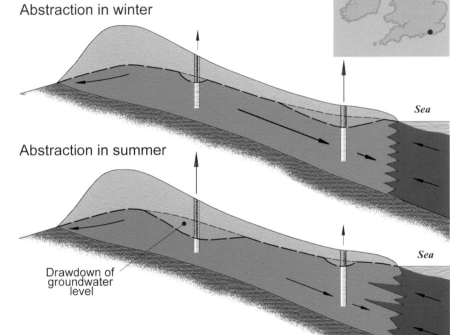

Seasonal abstraction patterns in the Chalk aquifer near Brighton. _The Chalk is a fractured limestone and saline intrusion penetrates inland along individual fractures. To reduce this tendency most of the abstraction in winter is near the coast to intercept the strong groundwater_ flow to the sea at this time. This conserves groundwater storage and allows water levels to recover in the aquifer. In summer most of the abstraction is from inland boreholes when groundwater flow to the sea is weaker. Abstraction from coastal boreholes is then reduced or stopped altogether._

Vulnerable aquifers need protection

Because aquifers are both porous and permeable, they are vulnerable to contamination from human activities associated with agricultural practices, urbanisation, industrial processes, disposal of wastes, and spillages of chemicals such as solvents and fuel oils. The threat can be from single sites or from a widespread use of the land as for example from agriculture. It can build up over many years and the exact cause may be difficult to identify.

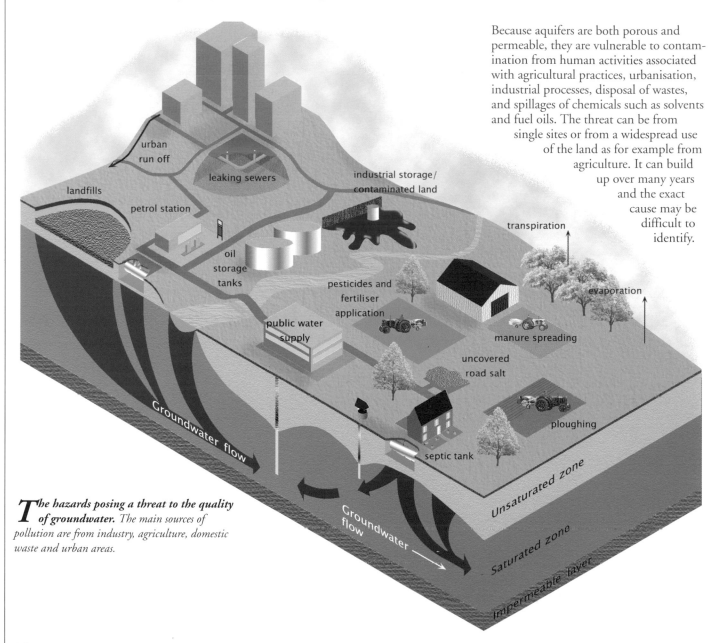

urban run off

leaking sewers

industrial storage/contaminated land

landfills

petrol station

oil storage tanks

transpiration

evaporation

pesticides and fertiliser application

public water supply

manure spreading

uncovered road salt

ploughing

septic tank

Groundwater flow

Groundwater flow

Unsaturated zone

Saturated zone

impermeable layer

The hazards posing a threat to the quality of groundwater. *The main sources of pollution are from industry, agriculture, domestic waste and urban areas.*

Vulnerable aquifers need protection

Restoring the groundwater in a contaminated aquifer to its original quality is both difficult and expensive. It is sensible to prevent, or at least reduce, the risk of contamination rather than deal with its consequences.

The vulnerability of an aquifer to contamination can be assessed from the composition of any overlying deposits, the nature and thickness of the unsaturated zone, and the speed with which water flows through the zone.

Groundwater Vulnerability Maps covering the UK have been prepared using these criteria and have been published by the environment agencies. They show which areas are more vulnerable to contamination and where it is necessary to protect groundwater from activities that are potentially polluting. The object is to protect the resource — the aquifer — from contamination.

There is also a need to protect individual groundwater sources — springs, wells and boreholes. Generally the closer a potentially polluting activity is to a source the greater the risk. Therefore, protection zones have been defined around sources used for public supply. Within these zones some activities and processes are either prohibited or restricted.

Groundwater is increasingly under threat in such a densely populated, industrial country as the UK. A threat to the quality of groundwater is a threat eventually to the entire aquatic environment as groundwater and surface water are so intimately linked.

Everyone has a role to play in protecting groundwater. An appreciation of the potential threats to its purity is an essential step to more prudent use of contaminating substances. Failure to comply can only lead to higher costs for the treatment of groundwater, costs that are inevitably met by the customer. Prevention of pollution is the best policy to ensure sustainable development of our precious water resources.

Thin sandy soil

Shallow water table

Fractured limestone

HIGH VULNERABILITY

Thick clayey soil

Thick boulder clay

Deep water table

Sand and gravel

LOW VULNERABILITY

The factors controlling the vulnerability of aquifers to pollution. Aquifers are best protected by a thick cover of clay and a thick unsaturated zone. Fractured limestones with a thin soil cover and a shallow water table are very vulnerable.

Vulnerable aquifers need protection

Source protection zones

Three protection zones have been defined around groundwater sources used for public supply. They vary in size and shape according to local conditions. The geology and the nature of the aquifer, the rainfall, the land use, and the amount of water pumped from the source, all have to be considered when defining their boundaries.

The Inner Zone I is defined by the distance a particle of water travels, through the saturated zone in 50 days.

*P*rotection zones around a borehole. Zone III covers the entire catchment area of the borehole. All the groundwater in the zone will eventually discharge into the borehole.

This distance, measured from the source, marks the outer boundary of the zone.

Additionally a minimum distance of 50 metres from the source is also stipulated. The 50-day time limit is based on the accepted principle that any bacteria in the saturated zone will die within 50 days.

Zone II is defined by the 400-day travel-time or 25% of the catchment area of the source whichever is the larger. In this case the travel time is based on the minimum time required for the dilution and attenuation of pollutants that degrade slowly.

Zone III is equivalent to the entire groundwater catchment of the source, that is the area from which the source derives its supply.

The weakness of applying 50-day and 400-day criteria is that they are based on a mean velocity of groundwater flow through an inter-granular aquifer. Where fractures are developed, flows that are faster than the assumed average are probable. However, the criteria are conservative to the extent that they only relate to flow in the saturated zone and do not take any account of the purifying action resulting from flow through the unsaturated zone.

Septic tanks

Households and other properties in rural areas may not be connected to public sewerage systems, and sewage effluents are often disposed of into the ground after they have passed through a septic tank.

A septic tank is a simple device which removes the suspended matter from sewage by settlement while the liquid fraction flows out of the tank and gradually infiltrates the ground from a subsurface drainage system of sand- or gravel-filled shallow trenches. The capacity of the soil and underlying rock to accept the liquid, that is their porosity and permeability, is an important factor in the design of such a disposal method. The solid fraction, retained in the tank, is broken down (or 'digested') by anaerobic decomposition. The liquid effluent is purified as it filters through the ground and it is attenuated by dilution with groundwater.

Septic tanks are an effective means of disposing of human waste in rural areas. Where many houses are concentrated in a small area, the discharge can lead to the contamination of groundwater, in particular by increasing the nitrate, sulphate and chloride concentrations.

The risk posed by the Channel Tunnel Rail Link

The high speed Channel Tunnel Rail Link will run from St Pancras Station, in London, to Folkestone, in Kent. The 88 kilometre route crosses the outcrops of

Vulnerable aquifers need protection

major and minor aquifers including the Chalk and the Lower Greensand.

The construction and subsequent operation of the line presents a threat to the quality of groundwater from polluted surface runoff, accidental spills of chemicals and hydrocarbons, the use of weedkillers, and the risk of collisions and derailments, particularly of freight traffic. Even small spills of some contaminants could pollute large volumes of groundwater for a very long time.

The route infringes the Groundwater Protection Zones, either Zones I, II, or III, of 14 major groundwater sources used for public supply. North and west of Maidstone, as far as the River Thames, the route will pass across the Chalk which is tapped by a number of boreholes, some as little as 20 metres from the proposed line of the track. The central section of the route crosses the Lower Greensand outcrop which provides water for the public supply boreholes in the confined aquifer to the north. All these sources fulfill a vital need for many small and large communities in south-east England.

The risk to the quality of groundwater and the security of so many public supply sources has been recognised by the promoters of the line. Steps will be taken to reduce the risk, principally by collecting drainage from the track and carrying it to safer discharge points away from the boreholes. The objective is to ensure that the water companies can continue to meet their statutory obligation of supplying water of an acceptable quality to the communities they serve.

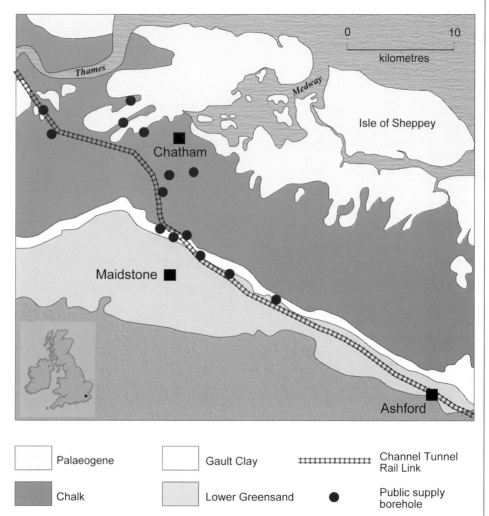

The proposed route of the Channel Tunnel Rail Link across Kent.
The route crosses Groundwater Protection Zones around the boreholes shown.

Palaeogene	Gault Clay	Channel Tunnel Rail Link
Chalk	Lower Greensand	● Public supply borehole

The nitrate problem

Sources of water supply for Nottingham and the surrounding region.

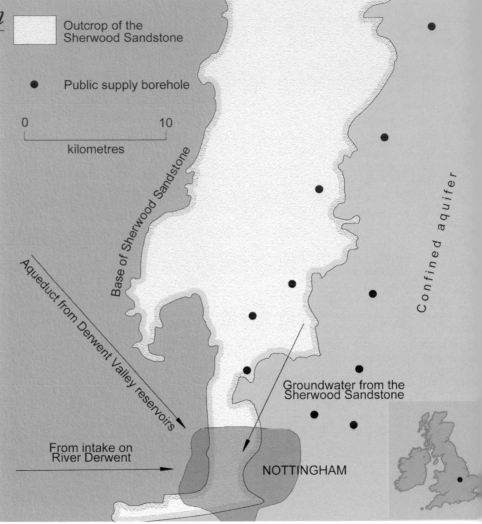

Nitrogen is an essential plant nutrient: some plants fix atmospheric nitrogen but modern farming practice involves the addition of nitrogen in the form of manure, sewage sludge and chemical fertilisers. The accumulation of soluble forms of nitrogen, particularly nitrate, in water can be detrimental since high concentrations in river water encourage eutrophication, and concentrations in drinking water must be limited for health reasons.

During and after the Second World War, as agriculture was gradually modernised, farming practices became much more intensive. Two changes had consequences for water quality. Firstly, large areas of virgin grassland were ploughed and this led to the oxidation of nitrogen in organic matter in the soil and, secondly, the application of artificial nitrogenous fertilisers to crops began to increase significantly in the 1950s. These changes increased the amount of nitrate leached from the soil by infiltrating rain and eventually a gradual but marked increase in the concentration in groundwater in the affected areas became evident in the early 1970s. Pollution from such widespread sources is referred to as diffuse contamination.

The rate of movement of water, and hence of nitrate, from the soil zone to the saturated zone is influenced by the depth of the water table, that is the thickness of the unsaturated zone, and the properties and nature of the aquifer. Water can pass quickly through fractured rocks, at rates of some tens of metres per day, but much more slowly through the matrix of chalk and sandstone. The velocity through the matrix of the Chalk is only about 1 m/year. Where the unsaturated zone is thick there can be a delay of many years before an increase in the amount of nitrate leached from the soil affects groundwater quality.

The nitrate concentration in groundwater is influenced by rainfall. Where the amounts of rainfall are low, the concentration tends to be high because the diluting

40

effect is reduced. Hence the worst affected areas are the drier eastern and central parts of England where the Chalk, the Permo-Triassic sandstones and the Lincolnshire Limestone are found at the surface.

Nitrate contamination is a long-term problem and remedial action is necessary. The cost of chemical treatment to remove it from groundwater is significant and disposal of waste products from the process can also be difficult. An alternative course is to reduce the contamination at the source — the amount leaching from the soil, which mainly occurs in the autumn and winter when the soil is fully saturated.

The scale of the problem can be reduced by better land management including:

- reducing the use of artificial fertilisers,

- reducing the extent of ploughing in the autumn,

- sowing autumn crops early,

- avoiding bare ground in the winter by sowing cover crops,

- delaying the ploughing-in of crop residues,

- carefully managing the disposal of farm wastes.

Nevertheless, despite more careful management, where the unsaturated zone is thick, it will be many years before beneficial effects from changes in farming practices are seen in the quality of groundwater.

Limiting the effect of nitrate

High concentrations of nitrate in drinking water can be detrimental to human health. Infants under one year old are particularly at risk from excessive amounts as it causes methaemoglobinaemia, commonly called 'blue baby syndrome'. A further concern is that nitrate can be converted, by bacteria in the digestive tract, into nitrosamines which are potentially carcinogenic. However, whether low levels of nitrate are harmful is often contested.

In 1980 the Drinking Water Directive of the European Community set a maximum limit for nitrate in water of 50 milligrams per litre (mg/l). On this basis many public-supply sources were providing groundwater with concentrations exceeding or close to the limit. In 1989 about 1% of the population of the UK was receiving water which failed to comply with the Directive and water from almost 200 public supply sources exceeded 50 mg/l at some time. Some boreholes were taken out of use, water from others was blended with low nitrate sources, and in yet others the water was treated to remove nitrate.

To guarantee better farming practices, firm direction in the form of legislation

was necessary. In 1991, the European Community issued a Nitrate Directive which requires states to identify waters that were or could be affected by nitrogen pollution from agricultural sources, and to designate as 'nitrate vulnerable zones' (NVZs) the land from which pollutants are derived.

The Government, in cooperation with the environment agencies, identified the public-supply sources abstracting groundwater that were susceptible to nitrate contamination and defined the recharge areas supplying these sources as possible NVZs. In 1996, after consultation with the farming community, 68 NVZs around groundwater sources were designated in England and Wales; two zones were proposed in Scotland. The Government will indicate measures that will have to be adopted in these zones to reduce the amount of nitrate that is leached from the soil. These should be incorporated into farming practices by the year 2000.

It is anticipated that these measures will be successful on the basis of a series of large-scale experiments that began in 1990. Ten groundwater catchments, subsequently increased to 32, were selected as 'Nitrate Sensitive Areas'. Farmers in these areas were offered payments in return for complying with rules for the use of fertiliser and manure, and the maintenance of a green ground cover in winter, and, in some areas, conversion of arable land to grassland. Nitrate leaching from some of these nitrate-sensitive areas has been reduced although it will be longer before the benefits to water supplies are realised.

The nitrate problem

Managing groundwater resources in south Nottinghamshire

Nottingham lies at the southern end of an extensive outcrop of the Triassic Sherwood Sandstone, which represents one of the largest groundwater reservoirs in the UK. Since the nineteenth century, the city has taken advantage of this to obtain water supplies from deep wells and boreholes in the sandstone. The aquifer is now fully developed and the long-term objective is to reduce abstraction to a sustainable level which will allow continuous use of the aquifer without damaging surface water features. This has already been partially achieved by reducing the quantities of water that can be abstracted under licence. At present the sandstone provides about 50% of the supply for the city and surrounding region.

The balance of the water requirements for the city is taken directly, by aqueduct, from surface reservoirs in the Derwent Valley, and from the River Derwent itself near Derby. The flow of the river is regulated by releasing water for this purpose from the Carsington Reservoir, in the Derwent Valley some 20 km north of Derby.

The concentration of nitrate in groundwater in the outcrop area of the Sherwood Sandstone has been steadily rising since the late 1960s. It now exceeds 50 mg/l over significant areas, exceeding the limit for drinking water stipulated by the European Union. This has been overcome by blending high-nitrate water from the outcrop with water from the confined aquifer, east of the outcrop, which contains water with a low nitrate concentration. New boreholes have been drilled in the confined zone and also in afforested areas on the outcrop of the sandstone, which also yield water with low concentrations of nitrate. Some areas on the outcrop of the sandstone, within catchments of public supply boreholes, have been designated 'Nitrate Sensitive Areas'. Within these areas farmers receive payments for changing farming practices, including reducing the application of fertiliser and manure, so as to reduce the amount of nitrate that can be leached from the soil.

Distribution of nitrate in groundwater in the outcrop of the Triassic Sherwood Sandstone of Nottinghamshire in 1993.
The map shows where values exceeded 50 mg/l. This is the maximum admissible concentration in drinking water as stipulated by the European Union.

Pesticides gain access to groundwater

Pesticide is a general term applied to herbicides, fungicides and insecticides that are used to kill pests and weeds. They are widely used for weed control in agriculture, on roads and railways, and to control pests in industry.

Synthetic organic pesticides were introduced during the Second World War and their use expanded rapidly in the 1950s and 1960s. By providing effective control of pests they have been a great benefit to agriculture and in conjunction with the use of fertilisers have increased crop yields considerably. However, by the early 1960s, undesirable effects on the environment were apparent. Rachael Carson drew attention to the risk to groundwater as long ago as 1962 in her classic book *Silent Spring*. But the measurement of pesticides at low concentration in water is complex and expensive, and the routine examination of groundwater for them is a recent event, as is a more widely perceived appreciation of their risk to groundwater quality.

The fate and behaviour of pesticides is controlled by the extent of their uptake by crops, and their susceptibility to leaching and degradation. Although their behaviour in the soil is relatively well known, in aquifers it is more obscure. Those that are soluble will clearly move through the unsaturated zone but their progress may be delayed by adsorption and they may degrade biologically, although the microbial population, and nutrients in the form of organic matter, are much reduced below the soil zone. Rapid flow through fractured aquifers poses a particular risk to groundwater quality.

Investigation of the distribution of pesticides in groundwater is in its early stages and the environment agencies are currently improving their monitoring programmes. However, it is clear that pesticides do occur in groundwater, albeit in small concentrations, generally below the EC maximum admissible concentration (MAC) of 0.1 microgram per litre. As their movement through the unsaturated zone is likely to be slow and measured in decades in many aquifers, studies of their distribution in this zone seems to be an essential step in defining the extent of the eventual problem in the saturated zone.

The water industry has introduced treatment processes to remove pesticides although the cost of treatment is high. Steps are also taken to encourage their careful use, storage and disposal, particularly near public supply boreholes. Some water companies have secured agreements with regular users of pesticides to restrict their use in areas where groundwater is susceptible to contamination.

Tractor spraying herbicide.

The risk from industrial chemicals

The exponential growth of the petrochemical and pharmaceutical industries in the 1950s introduced a wide range of complex organic wastes into the urban environment. A serious risk to groundwater quality has arisen from accidental spills or leaks from tanks and pipelines of petroleum products, phenols and chlorinated hydrocarbons. Some of these substances are soluble in water but many are only slightly soluble. The latter are referred to as non-aqueous phase liquids (or NAPLs) and they are divided into light and dense NAPLs according to whether they are less or more dense than water. Light NAPLs are mainly petroleum products and the dense variety include the chlorinated hydrocarbons widely used as industrial solvents. The concentration of these compounds allowed in drinking water is in the parts per billion range. Many are sufficiently soluble to make it possible to exceed these very low limits.

When a NAPL is spilled on the surface of a sandstone, it infiltrates slowly down through the unsaturated zone moving from pore to pore once the saturation of the hydrocarbon exceeds a threshold known as the residual saturation. The volume of the contaminant that is mobile steadily decreases because some is retained in each pore at the residual saturation. Thus with a small spill the contaminant may be retained entirely in the unsaturated zone once all the spill is at residual saturation in the rocks. With a larger or continuous spill the NAPL will eventually reach the capillary fringe. As it moves down through the unsaturated zone it also spreads laterally, because capillary forces as well as gravity control its migration. In fractured rocks progress may be much more rapid with the contaminant following the most permeable route.

When the NAPL reaches the capillary fringe, if it is a light NAPL, it will accu-

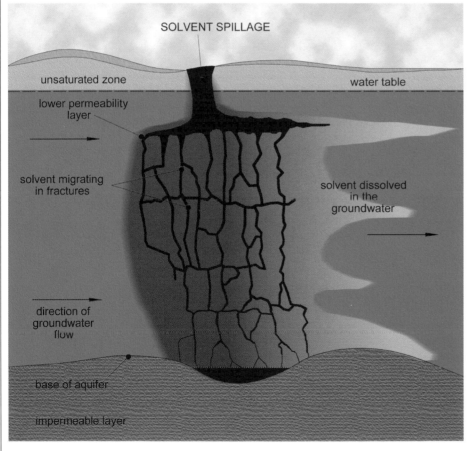

Pollution of the Chalk by the solvent tetrachloroethylene (a dense NAPL). Migration of the pollutant below the water table is retarded by a layer of chalk of low permeability. Below this layer the pollutant is migrating in the fractures in the aquifer and collecting at the base. Pollutant dissolved in groundwater is migrating through the aquifer in the direction of groundwater flow.

SOLVENT SPILLAGE

unsaturated zone

water table

lower permeability layer

solvent migrating in fractures

solvent dissolved in the groundwater

direction of groundwater flow

base of aquifer

impermeable layer

mulate near the top and flow in the direction of the hydraulic gradient once a critical thickness is attained. The contaminant continues to spread until the entire spill is at residual saturation.

When a dense NAPL reaches the capillary fringe, downward flow continues as before once the residual saturation of each pore is exceeded. This continues until it reaches the base of the aquifer. The contaminant then moves down the gradient of the base of the aquifer, again until the entire spill is at residual saturation. The direction of flow in this case may not coincide with the hydraulic gradient.

Pollution of an aquifer by NAPLs can increase by slow dissolution in groundwater. The resulting contaminant plume can be much larger than the spread of the spill itself and, because of the slow rate of dissolution, can persist as a source of pollution for decades.

Light NAPLs are more easily controlled as they float on the water table and occur at relatively shallow depths. Dense NAPLs move under the influence of their density and can penetrate to considerable depths. Once an aquifer is contaminated it is likely to remain so as remedial measures tend to be ineffective.

A single spill has the potential to contaminate a very large volume of water to levels in excess of the low concentration acceptable in drinking water. The wide distribution of petrol stations and the extensive networks of pipelines carrying petroleum products illustrates the potential risk to groundwater quality.

A spill of the solvent tetrachloroethylene, a dense NAPL, at a leather-processing factory in Cambridgeshire, polluted the Chalk to a depth of 50 m and extended for at least 2 km in the direction of groundwater flow. A major public water supply pumping station became contaminated. Because of the scale of the spill and the gradual dissolution of the contaminant in the groundwater, the contamination is likely to persist for many years.

At present the water industry must combat the threat by treating polluted water or replacing the source — both are very expensive options to overcome a problem largely caused by carelessness.

Prevention is cheaper than cure

The Groundwater Protection Policy of the environment agencies sets out a framework of guidance within which everyone can ensure groundwater resources are safeguarded for the future. One advantage is that developments which pose a risk to the quality of groundwater can be assessed at the planning stage and if necessary modified or even rejected.

An example that poses a particular risk is a petrol filling station on an aquifer such as the Chalk, particularly if it is close to a public supply borehole.

The very fractured nature of the Chalk, and its resulting high permeability, provides a ready passage for the flow of pollutants from the ground surface to the water table. In this situation a petrol station on the Chalk undoubtedly poses a considerable risk to groundwater quality. It is unacceptable in Zone I and should be discouraged in Zones II and III around a public supply borehole.

Modern petrol stations should incorporate a multi-layered system to contain any leakage from their storage tanks or the forecourt. These include double-skinned tanks in a concrete vault lined with synthetic polymer membranes, and compacted clay. In the short-term these precautions do afford an adequate safeguard, but components deteriorate, concrete cracks, synthetic membranes may be breached, and, as the integrity of such a system cannot be monitored in a practical manner, it does not provide a reliable effective long-term barrier against leakage.

What may be immediately at risk from a petrol station is a source of public water supply providing perhaps 5 million litres of water per day for some 30 000 people. The Drinking Water Standard for dissolved or emulsified hydrocarbons is only 10 micrograms per litre (that is 1 part per 100 million parts of water). Once a fine-grained aquifer such as the Chalk is contaminated it is well nigh impossible to clean it up to drinking water standards. The cost of a replacement water supply could be least £5 million. The careful assessment of

The risk from industrial chemicals

planning applications for the storage of chemicals in a Groundwater Protection Zone is, therefore, a wise precaution.

The disposal of radioactive waste

Much concern has been expressed about the safe disposal of radioactive waste. For the general public it has become an emotive subject as the waste remains radioactive for many years and unless proper safety precautions are taken radiation can be a risk to health.

Classification of radioactive waste

- Low-level waste, mainly discarded clothing and wrapping materials. It comprises about 90% of the total volume of radioactive waste and represents only a small risk.

- Intermediate-level waste comprising metal fuel cladding, reactor components and chemical sludges. It forms 10% of the total waste volume and has a long lifespan of radioactive decay. This waste must be shielded from the environment and an option is disposal in a deep repository.

- High-level waste arising from reprocessing nuclear fuel. It comprises only 0.1% of the total but contains 95% of the radioactivity. The current policy is to store this waste at the surface in a vitrified form, until its temperature has dropped sufficiently to allow safe disposal.

Small amounts of very low-level radioactive waste have been disposed of in landfills, but most low-level waste is deposited in concrete vaults and trenches in glacial deposits at Drigg, near Sellafield in Cumbria.

A favoured preference for the disposal of intermediate-level waste, and also longer-lived low-level waste, which cannot be disposed of at Drigg, is deep disposal in an underground repository, constructed at a depth of about 1 km in very impermeable rocks.

The objective is to take advantage of the fact that water in such rocks is extremely old, very saline and is moving exceedingly slowly. To guard against the risk of contaminating the biosphere, the concept behind such deep burial is to provide a containment facility with several barriers to prevent the migration of the radionuclides. This is referred to as the multi-barrier containment concept.

The wastes, in steel or concrete containers would be placed in excavated chambers in the rock which would then be backfilled with a cement-based material. The backfill would have a high surface area to adsorb radionuclides, and it would maintain alkaline conditions in the pore waters and thereby suppress the solubility of important radionuclides. The host rock itself would provide a final barrier with a long pathway and time of travel in slowly moving groundwater to the biosphere. Any radionuclides that entered the groundwater, slowly flowing through the rocks, would be retarded by adsorp-

tion and diffusion into the rock matrix. The concept makes use of engineering, chemical and natural barriers to achieve long-term containment.

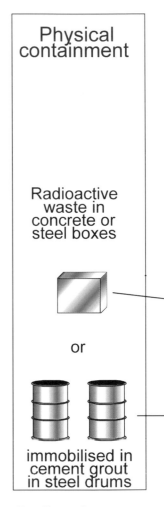

Physical containment

Radioactive waste in concrete or steel boxes

or

immobilised in cement grout in steel drums

Radioactive waste in containers

The multi-barrier containment concept for the disposal of low-level and intermediate-level radioactive wastes.

Uniform chemical conditions

- Alkaline chemistry
- High sorption capacity

Disposal vault

Cement backfill material

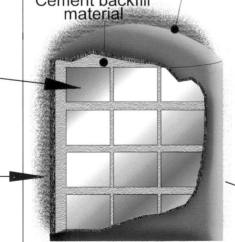

Surrounded by a cement-based backfill

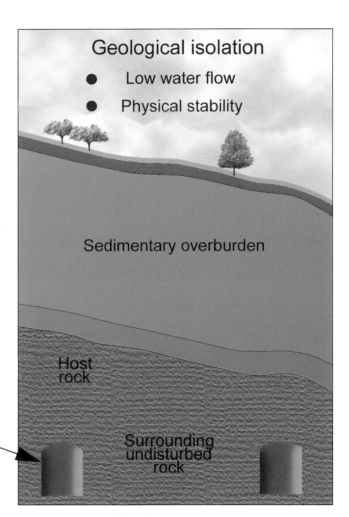

Geological isolation

- Low water flow
- Physical stability

Sedimentary overburden

Host rock

Surrounding undisturbed rock

Lies in a deep cavern in an impermeable host rock

Leachates from landfills

Each year over 150 million tonnes of solid waste from domestic, commercial and industrial sources are disposed of in landfills. The waste ranges from inert waste with a low polluting potential to hazardous chemical wastes. Landfilling is often the cheapest disposal option.

Solid wastes pose a threat to groundwater quality through the formation of polluting liquids known as leachates.

Cross-section of a modern landfill. The design incorporates a synthetic membrane liner (about 2.5 millimetres thick) on a layer of low-permeability clay (about 1 metre thick). The leachate is drained to a sump by a network of pipes in a permeable drainage layer. Any gas generated is collected by means of a system of pipes. (Not drawn to scale).

These form as water percolates through the waste, dissolving soluble compounds and the degradation products of chemical and biochemical reactions that take place in the waste. Domestic solid waste gives rise to a very polluting leachate. It decomposes under anaerobic conditions after a brief aerobic stage of a few months; a final stage leads to the production of methane, by which time the polluting strength of the leachate is reduced. The entire decomposition process can take decades, the rate being very much a function of the amount of water that can gain access to the waste.

There are thousands of landfills in the UK. Many are old or disused and now classified as 'contaminated land'. Modern landfills are carefully constructed so that the liquid waste products are contained. In the past it was considered acceptable to allow

leachates to seep from the base of the waste into underlying rocks where they were diluted by the groundwater and gradually dispersed through the ground. Percolation through rock does improve the quality of leachates and reduces their polluting strength but such processes are not entirely reliable and any risk of polluting groundwater in this manner is not now acceptable.

Instead landfills are lined with clay and flexible synthetic membranes, intended to prevent leachate escaping and contaminating groundwater. The leachate is drained to collecting sumps for subsequent treatment. Methane is also collected and either vented to the atmosphere, or used for heating, or even the generation of electricity.

The current disposal practice is designed to create very compact dense waste which effectively reduces its contact with water.

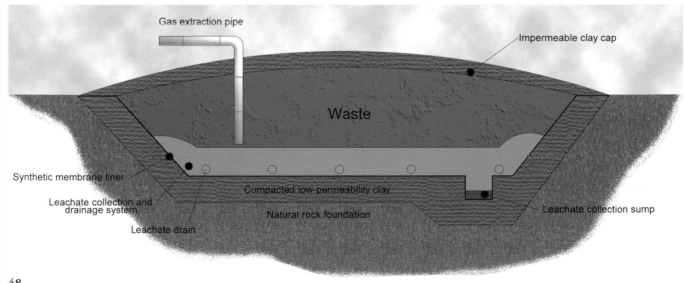

Gas extraction pipe

Impermeable clay cap

Waste

Synthetic membrane liner

Leachate collection and drainage system

Leachate drain

Compacted low-permeability clay

Natural rock foundation

Leachate collection sump

Leachates from landfills

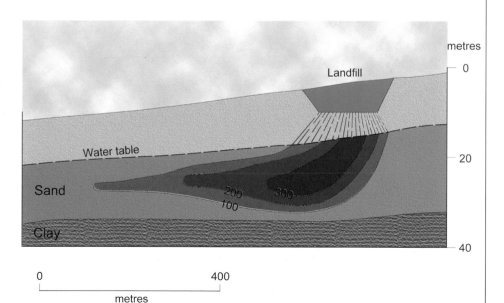

Laying a liner of synthetic membrane for a new landfill.

Furthermore, the waste is covered with a layer of clay to prevent, or at least reduce, the ingress of surface water. This practice reduces the rate of decomposition. It may be decades before leachate and gas are produced, especially in the large and deep sites that are now favoured. Recent views are that water should not be excluded and that ideally landfills should be very efficient bioreactors with high rates of leachate formation and accelerated rates of decomposition. A landfill should reach a final, stable unpolluting state within about 30 years. This could mean that it is necessary to irrigate the waste with water or recycle the leachate to encourage decomposition.

Landfill operators are required to have a licence from one of the environment agencies and to adhere to waste management licensing regulations. Landfills must be designed and constructed to high engineering standards to ensure containment of waste products and thereby provide long-term protection of the environment. However, although much is known about the processes in a landfill, monitoring facilities around sites and the assessment of the performance of sites are relatively undeveloped. There are no well-defined standards of performance.

The efficacy of the long-term containment of wastes has yet to be demonstrated and the overall risk to groundwater quality remains uncertain. However, although landfills are potential threats to groundwater quality, any pollution that occurs is localised and quite dissimilar to the more widespread pollution that arises from agriculture and from urban areas. Nevertheless, reducing the polluting impact of landfills remains a prime consideration.

Migration of a plume of leachate from a landfill. The high chloride concentrations in the groundwater (the units are milligrams per litre) show the extent of the plume. Landfills are now designed so that leachates are contained in the structure and collected for appropriate disposal. Contamination of underlying aquifers should not occur.

metres

Landfill

Water table

Sand

200

100

300

Clay

0

20

40

0

400

metres

49

Contaminated land and urban pollution

Contaminated land and urban pollution are legacies of the Industrial Revolution and the subsequent industrial expansion. For over 200 years industrial wastes have been disposed of, and spilled in and near urban areas, and many contain potential groundwater contaminants. Initially they were mainly mining and foundry wastes, essentially inorganic compounds, but eventually they included tars, phenolic wastes, oils and, more recently, complex synthetic organic compounds. These and similar substances have contaminated large areas of land particularly in urban areas but also around mines, military installations and old landfills.

Land contaminated in this manner can give rise to a range of liquid and gaseous pollutants, and the more soluble and mobile infiltrate to the water table. Below many industrial sites there are plumes of contaminated groundwater slowly moving down the hydraulic gradient.

It has been estimated that over 500 square kilometres of contaminated land exist in the UK distributed over more than 50 000 sites, although only some pose a threat to the quality of groundwater. A particular risk arises when sites are redeveloped, as this disturbs and may remobilise pollutants.

Land is contaminated when substances are present at concentrations that could be harmful to humans, animals or the environment as a whole. To pose a risk there must be a source of contamination, a pathway that allows the contaminant to migrate, and a specific location (or target) which may be affected. To put this in a groundwater context with a typical example, old gasworks produced coal, or 'town', gas until the mid-1960s, contaminating the ground underlying the works with compounds including coal tar, phenols, cyanides, heavy metals and sulphur compounds. These substances were dissolved by infiltrating water and the groundwater became contaminated over a much greater area. If the groundwater flowed to a borehole or well used as a source of drinking water, then the risk sequence was completed.

The decontamination of such a site may involve pumping and treating the groundwater, as well as the removal of the contaminated soil to landfills, or the treatment of the soil on site by one of the remedial methods available. Such land reclamations are obviously extremely costly.

The scale and nature of the problem of contaminated land in urban areas and around industrial complexes remains uncertain. Currently this is being assessed by the environment agencies. There is not a national register of contaminated land but local authorities will have to compile their own registers, and have powers to investigate potential problems

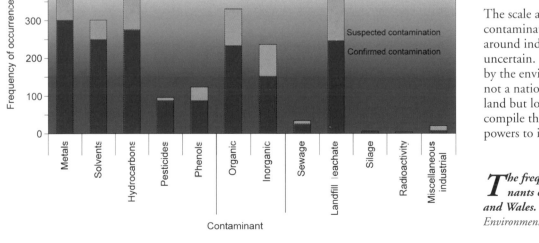

The frequency that particular contaminants occur in groundwater in England and Wales. The data are from a survey by the Environment Agency of groundwater pollution.

and require remediation where a risk to the environment or public health can be demonstrated. The onus for cleaning-up contaminated land, however, is with the owner.

Generally it can be assumed that urban areas are centres of groundwater pollution from industrial zones, railways, and possibly leaking sewers. Studies of the quality of groundwater below the cities of Birmingham and Coventry revealed that pollution by organic and inorganic compounds was extensive. The predominant organic pollutants were chlorinated hydrocarbon solvents. There was a close correlation between land use and the pollutants identified. Widespread contamination of groundwater by solvents in the Chalk below Luton has also been recorded.

A recent survey of the extent of groundwater pollution in England and Wales, by the Environment Agency, revealed that the main sources of pollution were landfills, the chemical and metal processing industries, and gas works, power stations and petrol service stations. The pollutants most frequently recorded were metals (particularly arsenic, copper and chromium), organic compounds and landfill leachates. The Chalk and the Triassic sandstones in the Midlands and north-west England were the aquifers particularly affected.

Usually the effect on groundwater is localised near the site in question, although in urban areas where there are many potential sources of pollution, con-

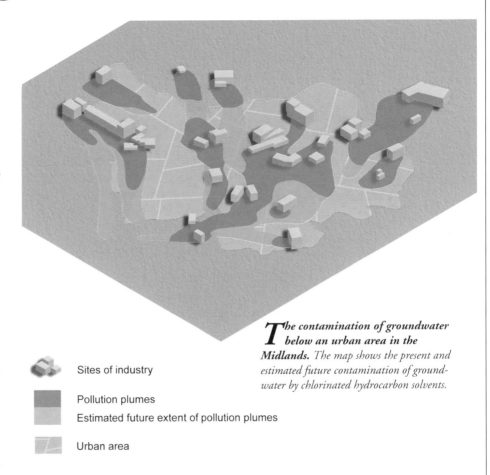

*T*he contamination of groundwater below an urban area in the **Midlands.** *The map shows the present and estimated future contamination of groundwater by chlorinated hydrocarbon solvents.*

Sites of industry

Pollution plumes

Estimated future extent of pollution plumes

Urban area

tamination is widespread, as in Coventry and Birmingham. Cleaning-up contaminated groundwater is of growing interest but the cost of clean-up set against the benefits that accrue is also an important consideration. In some situations, for example where the groundwater is not likely to be used for drinking, less stringent levels of 'clean-up' may be appropriate. The question that must be answered is: does the contamination pose a potential risk to human health, or the environment, on the basis of current and anticipated use of the site or area?

Remedies for pollution

On-site treatment of groundwater pumped from an aquifer contaminated by chlorinated hydrocarbons.

If groundwater is contaminated by a relatively small-scale source of pollution such as a spill of hydrocarbons, the question is: how can the quality be restored or at least improved to an acceptable standard?

There are four basic remediation methods:

● Containment of the pollutant, that is, prevent it spreading by using physical barriers such as sheet piles, cement grouts and impermeable membranes.

● Removal of the contaminated water by pumping and then treating it to an appropriate quality. The water can then be either re-injected into the aquifer or used directly for water supply.

The first concern is to determine the distribution of the contaminant in the aquifer, whether it is in the unsaturated zone or the saturated zone or both, and whether it is entirely in solution or there is a non-aqueous phase. Answers to these questions will suggest a possible remediation strategy as shown below.

Despite the availability of these techniques, restoring an aquifer to its original pristine state is difficult if not impossible. When a contaminated aquifer is pumped, the groundwater flows preferentially through the more permeable horizons and consequently these are cleaned relatively easily and quickly. However, contaminants that have penetrated into less permeable horizons and the smaller pore spaces may be virtually unaffected. When pumping stops, contaminants from these zones diffuse into the permeable zones that have

● Removal of the volatile fraction of a contaminant by a process called 'bioventing'. Soil gas is removed by vacuum pumping from a borehole. This circulates air which volatilises and assists in the degradation of organic contaminants. The method removes volatile contaminants from an aquifer that are present at less than the residual saturation level.

● Bioremediation to deal with organic contaminants. The technique is intended to encourage bacteria to grow by adding nutrients to the contaminated zone.

been cleared. The more permeable fractures in the Chalk represent only 1 or 2% of the total rock volume while the relatively immobile water in the matrix represents 25 to 40%; in this situation the cleaning process can take a very long time. Similarly, if nutrients are injected to encourage biodegradation they may penetrate only slowly into the less permeable horizons.

The difficulty of cleaning an aquifer emphasises the need to minimise all forms of pollution. Where it does occur the problem should be tackled at or as near the source as possible and as soon as possible after the event. It must be accepted that with existing technology groundwater quality often cannot be restored within a reasonable time and at a reasonable cost. Nevertheless, wherever pollution occurs in an aquifer it should be contained and treatment initiated, bearing in mind the use made of the groundwater, any health risk that exists and the cost.

Organic matter is degraded into simple compounds such as water and carbon dioxide. Alternatively, specific bacteria can be introduced to metabolise a particular contaminant. The process can be encouraged by injecting air into the contaminated zone from a borehole. This stimulates aerobic biodegradation. Under favourable conditions, bioremediation can occur as a result of natural processes in an aquifer. Indigenous microbes will degrade organic contaminants if a supply of nutrients is present for their metabolism.

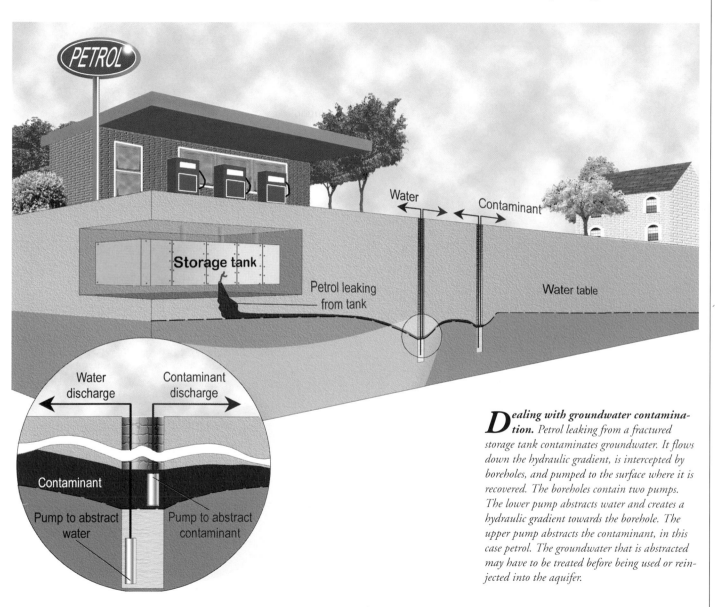

PETROL

Water
Contaminant

Storage tank

Petrol leaking
from tank

Water table

Water
discharge

Contaminant
discharge

Contaminant

Pump to abstract
water

Pump to abstract
contaminant

Dealing with groundwater contamination. *Petrol leaking from a fractured
storage tank contaminates groundwater. It flows
down the hydraulic gradient, is intercepted by
boreholes, and pumped to the surface where it is
recovered. The boreholes contain two pumps.
The lower pump abstracts water and creates a
hydraulic gradient towards the borehole. The
upper pump abstracts the contaminant, in this
case petrol. The groundwater that is abstracted
may have to be treated before being used or rein-
jected into the aquifer.*

Mine drainage

Coal and metalliferous mines can be hundreds of metres deep, with the workings well below the natural water table. Consequently, deep mining is only possible if mines are drained by pumping. At the time of maximum coal output from mines in England and Wales some 450 million cubic metres of water were pumped each year for drainage purposes. The collieries of South Wales and Scotland were particularly wet, pumping 8 and 10 cubic metres of water, respectively, per tonne of coal mined, although the average drainage-output ratio for collieries in England and Wales as a whole was 2 cubic metres per tonne of coal.

Coal seams and mudstones in the Coal Measures contain pyrite (ferrous sulphide) which was subject to oxidation by air as the water table was lowered, the process being supported by sulphur-oxidising bacteria. As a result water draining from coal mines can be very acidic, with pH values of 2 or 3, due to sulphuric acid, and high concentrations of sulphate and iron, as well as other metals, in solution. Similar waters form in metalliferous mines and in mine wastes.

The discharge of such waters to rivers is detrimental. The iron precipitates as ferric hydroxide when the pH rises above 6, following reactions with the river sediments and mixing with alkaline waters in rivers, and when bacterial oxidation of the ferrous compounds occurs. The iron precipitate discolours the rivers leaving unsightly ochrous deposits and the oxidation process leads to the depletion of the oxygen in the river water.

Ferruginous waters discharging from disused mines have been a problem for decades, but with the closure of so many coalmines, beginning in the 1950s and continuing into the 1990s, the problem has been accentuated. As mines closed, pumping stopped or was reduced and groundwater levels recovered. The rate of recovery depends very much on the rate of flow into the workings and their extent. In some cases complete recovery may take several decades. As well as contaminating rivers, rising acidic ferruginous groundwater may in the future contaminate aquifers overlying the Coal Measures such as the Permian Basal Sands, the Magnesian Limestone and the Permo-Triassic sandstones. The rise of water levels can also lead to subsidence as a result of the weakening and eventual collapse of strata left to support the roof in shallow workings. The corrosion of engineering structures that contain Portland Cement and the flooding of landfills are other problems.

The quality of the discharge from disused mines improves gradually with time as the rising groundwater flushes the acidic oxidation products out of the Coal Measures, but the process can take many years.

Increasingly widespread pollution by such acidic ferruginous waters seems to be inevitable unless expensive treatment methods are introduced or pumping from some mines is continued to control the discharges. The circulation of contaminated ferruginous waters through artificially constructed wetlands, which improves their quality, is being investigated as a relatively cheap solution to the problem.

Responsibility for pollution by acid mine-waters is very unclear. Mine owners who permit pollution from abandoned mines are given indemnity under the Water Resources Act of 1991 and, in Scotland, the Control of Pollution Act of 1974. The Environment Act 1995 has removed this defence but only for mines abandoned after 1999. This leaves the legal responsibility and the problem unresolved.

The rebound of groundwater levels in coalfields

The recovery of groundwater levels in coalfields that are no longer mined has caused serious environmental problems in many areas and potential future problems in others. The coalfields in Scotland afford numerous examples, a case in point being the Dalquharran Colliery in Ayrshire, where pumping for drainage purposes ceased in 1977. Groundwater levels recovered and water began discharging from the mine in 1979 at rates rising to 13 Ml/d. The water flowed into the River Girvan. As it contained 1200 mg/l of iron, 100 mg/l of aluminium and 6000 mg/l of sulphate, the effect on the ecology of the river was devastating. The problem was ameliorated by adding lime to the outflow and controlling the rate so as to link it to the flow of the river, thereby ensuring dilution.

The mine workings in the Durham Coalfield are extensively interconnected. While the collieries were operating, groundwater levels were maintained some 150 metres below the ground surface by pumping almost 100 Ml/day from nine pumping shafts. The quality of the water was quite good and most was discharged into the River Wear providing nearly 50% of the flow in dry spells. Once this pumping stops the rising groundwater will dissolve the oxidation products of pyrite in the Coal Measures to give an acidic water, with large concentrations of metal ions in solution, which will discharge ultimately into the river system. The Permian aquifers that overlie the Coal Measures are also likely to be contaminated. Complete recovery of groundwater levels in the Durham Coalfield may take 30 or 40 years.

Contamination of the River Esk in East Lothian *by ferruginous groundwater discharging from an abandoned coal mine.*

The future role of groundwater

For 200 years groundwater has provided a reliable, very economic water supply for a large part of an increasingly industrialised and urbanised nation. The steady increase in demand for water has created a situation where the groundwater resources of the main aquifers are fully developed in many areas and over-developed in some.

This began to become evident by the middle of the century. At about the same time the impact of groundwater abstraction on some rivers became apparent, particularly those draining the Chalk in south-east England. These events led to the introduction in the 1960s of a policy of using surface water and groundwater in conjunction, a practice expected to be used increasingly in the future. Greater use will be made of the storage capacity of aquifers to meet short-term peak demands; aquifers will be used seasonally when surface water is in short supply; artificial recharge will be introduced to replenish depleted storage in aquifers.

Excessive use of groundwater has been blamed for the decline of river flows. Undoubtedly this is correct in some cases and it is now accepted that groundwater has the dual function of providing for water supply and preserving the aquatic environment. As appropriate, and where practical, groundwater will continue to be pumped from boreholes into rivers to preserve and augment flows in dry periods. However, it must not be overlooked that during droughts, springs do dry up naturally and this raises the difficult question of whether at times of water shortages groundwater should be pumped into rivers merely to

Principal elements of the Lancashire Conjunctive Use Scheme.

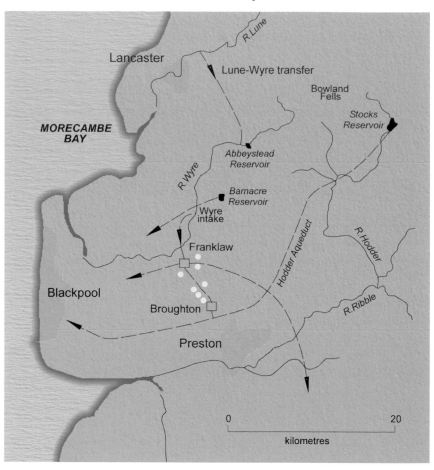

---- ------ ------ ------   Aqueducts

☐   Treatment works

River intakes

Groups of water supply boreholes

preserve the aquatic environment, in effect to maintain an 'unnatural' flow.

In the context of future developments the possibility of a change in the climate is very relevant. The balance of evidence is that the emission of carbon dioxide and other gases from man's activities is trapping infra-red radiation in the atmosphere and steadily warming it. An understanding of how this will alter the climate of the UK and affect groundwater resources remains uncertain. A likely scenario is that, although replenishment of aquifers in winter will be similar to, or even higher than at present, summers will be warmer and drier. This type of weather will possibly extend into the autumn delaying the seasonal replenishment of aquifers. Warmer summers would lead to greater demands for water particularly for irrigation. A sequence of dry winters would be more serious than

at present. The pressure on water resources would be felt especially in the south and east of England where the main aquifers occur. In these circumstances even greater attention would have to be devoted to the management of aquifers to make the most effective use of the large volume of water stored in them.

In this short account about groundwater, much attention has been devoted to the risk of the contamination of groundwater resources. But this should be kept in perspective. Many pollution incidents from landfills, or contaminated land, or leaking pipes are only local problems. Contamination from diffuse sources, such as agricultural land, the use of pesticides and the seepage from industrial areas, creates more widespread difficulties that have to be dealt with by reducing the source of the pollution or treating the water at the well-head before distribution for supply.

Nevertheless, the fact remains that groundwater is basically a water of very good quality. Those who are provided with it for drinking purposes should appreciate this. Groundwater is the largest store of fresh water and it will be increasingly used as part of integrated water resource management systems — optimising the use of rivers, surface reservoirs and aquifers. Everyone should help to maintain the quality of groundwater for it is a priceless natural resource — a truly national asset.

*T**he operation of the Lancashire Conjunctive Use Scheme over a calendar year.** The surface reservoirs provide supplies throughout the year, river water supplements them during the winter and groundwater during the summer. The figures are the percentages each source contributes to the total design output of the scheme.*

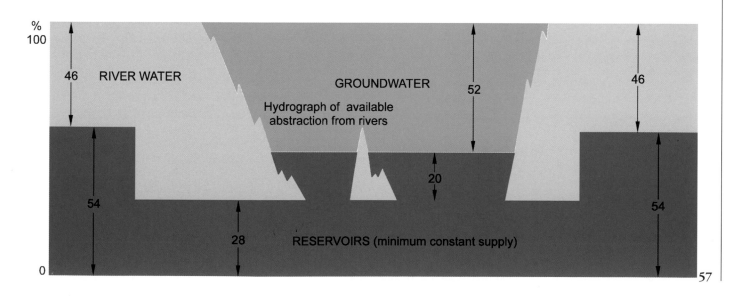

The future role of groundwater

A*n experimental artificial recharge basin in the Triassic sandstones of Nottinghamshire.* *River water was recharged into the sandstones after basic treatment, at an average rate of 0.36 metres per day.*

Benefits from the combined use of water resources

The optimal development of water resources requires the use of the surface and groundwater resources as a single integrated system. In its simplest form, surface water is used when it is plentiful and groundwater is reserved for periods of below-average rainfall, when surface resources cannot meet all the demands. One of the first schemes to make use of this concept was the Lancashire Conjunctive Use Scheme which was developed to provide water for the communities of central and south Lancashire. The scheme exploits the Triassic sandstones of the Flyde, north of Preston, together with surface water stored in the Stocks and Barnacre reservoirs in the Bowland Forest of Lancashire. Water is also transferred from the River Lune, near Lancaster, to augment the flow of the River Wyre and provide water for public supply by means of an intake at Garstang. The Triassic sandstones, which are up to 500 metres thick, are developed by over 40 boreholes each about 150 metres deep and yielding between 1 and 6 Ml/d. Groundwater is also discharged into the River Wyre to augment the flow during extended periods of dry weather.

The maximum licensed output of the scheme is over 180 Ml/d, much greater than would be the case if each source was operated separately. The Lancashire Conjunctive Use Scheme is now linked into a much larger regional network of water sources and distribution systems in north-west England.

THE PRIORITIES FOR GROUNDWATER MANAGEMENT

- SUSTAINABLE LONG-TERM YIELDS FROM AQUIFERS

- EFFECTIVE USE OF THE LARGE VOLUME OF WATER STORED IN AQUIFERS

- PRESERVATION OF GROUNDWATER QUALITY

- PRESERVATION OF THE AQUATIC ENVIRONMENT BY PRUDENT ABSTRACTION OF GROUNDWATER

- INTEGRATION OF GROUNDWATER AND SURFACE WATER INTO A COMPREHENSIVE WATER AND ENVIRONMENTAL MANAGEMENT SYSTEM

TO PROTECT A PRICELESS NATIONAL ASSET

The **Environment Agency** has a duty to operate to high professional standards based on ".... sound science, information and analysis of the environment and of processes which affect it". To help it discharge this duty it has established a number of National Centres in order to concentrate resources and expertise.

The **National Groundwater and Contaminated Land Centre** is one of these. Its main objectives are:

- to ensure that the Agency approaches and deals with groundwater and contaminated land issues and decision making in a consistent manner;
- to provide an expert advisory service for Environment Agency staff and to keep abreast of technical developments nationally and internationally;
- to assist in the training and technical development of staff;
- to manage projects including relevant aspects of the R & D programme;
- to provide an expert advisory role in the development of policy and in reviewing its implementation;
- to support the Agency in its links with national and international organisations;
- to undertake a technical leadership role and provide a technical focus for external bodies.

Environment Agency, National Groundwater & Contaminated Land Centre, Olton Court, 10 Warwick Road, Olton, Solihull B92 7HX
Tel: +44 (0)121 711 2324   Fax: +44 (0)121 711 5130   e-mail: ngwclc@dial.pipex.com

The **Hydrogeology Group** of the British Geological Survey, comprises over 40 hydrogeoscientists with wide experience of groundwater research in Britain and throughout the world. We manage the National Groundwater Archive, a unique database which is used as a basis for our Hydrogeological Enquiry Service.

The Group's main areas of expertise are:

- groundwater mapping, field surveying and resource evaluation
- assessment of agricultural, urban and industrial groundwater pollution
- groundwater quality and hydrochemical processes
- water quality, gas and isotope analysis and evaluation
- groundwater management and protection
- computer modelling of groundwater flow, quality and well hydraulics
- evaluation of aquifer physical properties and heterogeneity

BGS is also the WHO Colloborating Centre on
Groundwater Quality Assessment and Protection

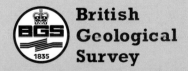

British Geological Survey, Hydrogeology Group, Maclean Building, Wallingford, UK, OX10 8BB
Tel: +44 (0)1491 838800   Fax: +44 (0)1491 692345   e-mail: hydrogeology@bgs.ac.uk